c.3   Rhodokanakēs
        Forever Ulysses

FC

FOREVER ULYSSES

FOREVER ULYSSES

A Novel by
C. P. RODOCANACHI

Translated by
Patrick Leigh-Fermor

New York

THE VIKING PRESS
Mcmxxxviii

First published in January 1938

Copyright 1938 by C. P. Rodocanachi
Printed in the United States of America
by H. Wolff Book Manufacturing Co.

This is not a story of any actual person, living or dead. The principal character is imaginary; no part of the book is to be read as biography. In seeking a synthesis of the modern Greek—eternal heir to the cunning of Ulysses, the courage of Achilles, the idealism of Plato—the author allowed his imagination to be guided by living models, adventurous Greeks of our own time whom he himself had met. But his Ulysses is no one of these. He is pure fiction—if fiction is the imaginative projection of the mind; and also pure truth—if truth is something deeper and more substantial than the mere outline of men and events.

—THE PUBLISHERS

FOREVER ULYSSES

1

✿✿

CEPHALONIA is the island where the Greek spirit reaches exasperation point. Having lost its ancient equilibrium, it treads with difficulty the tight-rope of moderation, usually falling off it into madness and, sometimes, into genius. Genius being, though the most dangerous of all evils, incurable, the Cephalonians are concerned only with their madmen. They employ, at great expense, a phrenologist who is famous throughout Greece: Saint Gerasymos. Hagiographers are vague about him. But the Greeks of every island and province, in search of a patron who will protect their sailing vessels and their local trade exclusively, without showering his favours on neighbouring provinces and islands, set little store by formal canonization. They choose a body, a slipper, a tooth, or some other relic, and weave their legends around it, beyond the ken of council and synod. More than one unknown pirate, having had the luck, or the misfortune, to be decapitated in some Turkish prison, enjoys the honours of beatitude, in the teeth of the patriarchs and metropolitans. The most famous instances are those of St. Constantine of Hydra, St. Patapios on the slopes of the Geranian mountains, and, in Athens even, St. Phanourios—who, all unknown to hagiographers, have unnumbered following.

Gerasymos, it would seem, is a saint of the highest order, and his legend is several centuries old. He is officially recognized, and his shrine stands on the side of a mountain that is far too high for so small an island. Everything in Cephalonia is exaggerated; the intelligence of the men, the virtue of the women, virtue itself, and, above all, vice.

The church of St. Gerasymos, which lies at the bottom of a deep valley where the immense shadow of Mount Ainos blurs the bustling shadows of the nuns and popes, is full, day and night, of madmen, howling, mewing, barking, whinnying, and braying, in an agony of exorcism, as the devil, deafened by the droning of the popes, chased by the incense that stifles him and the signs of the cross that he abhors, howls, mews, barks, whinnies, and brays through the mouths of the victims whom St. Gerasymos snatches from his grasp. This delirium of deliverance continues throughout the year; but when the feast day of the Saint draws nigh, all the roadways are black with the madmen whom the lunatic monks push or pull towards the healer; for all roads, in Cephalonia, lead to St. Gerasymos. His renown is such that, when a Cephalonian swears by "the

[8]

Saint"—the name being understood—one can almost believe him. Beneath the Saint's invoked protection, the island's exports have been of the highest quality. Since the seventeenth century, she has provided the King of Siam with a prime minister, the last Emperor of Brazil with a favourite, and the Madagascans with a saint. That this saint should have fled his village after stabbing a comrade over a game of dice casts no stain on the unspotted reputation that he succeeded in establishing in his new country.

One day, some of his former countrymen, passing through Madagascar, visited his tomb. When they fell to exchanging tales about his life and laughing over his mischievous tricks, the pious Madagascans, prostrate before his miraculous remains, took umbrage, and the sceptics almost proved with their lives the truth that a prophet is nothing in his own country.

Between Corfu, singing in the shade of her olive trees, and flower-clad Zante playing her mandolin, Cephalonia, strong and melancholy, meditates. Of the purest Doric blood, stern with himself and with his neighbour, the Cephalonian holds his peace, like a prisoner planning escape; first, from the limits of his narrow island, later, from one lost adventure to another, the dream of which may have caught his fancy.

Never having known Turkish slavery, never having submitted to Venetian or British influence (for all enterprise slides over him, as over the coat of the hedgehog, till the spines stand up and wound the hand that would grasp him), the Cephalonian is, today, the most Greek of all the Greeks.

There is something of the cities of old about the island villages. They are divided into clans, and arranged on either side of a main street that curls through bastioned angles and between lofty walls unbroken by door or window. The mean back lanes that wind clandestinely down to the main street are the only means of communication. Behind these walls, the husbands and fathers were safe from the attacks of the wild corsairs, and the women from the still more dreaded glance of other men.

On a winter night in one of these villages, a child was born. The howling of the wind drowned its first mewling wails. The villagers called him the child of the storm. He came unminded into the world, like animals and all humble creatures. Only the old grandmother, poking up the ashes where she was making coffee for her daughter-in-law, encouraged her from a distance, repeating the advice of many generations' experience. The child was suckled haphazard, after the manner of young goat kids, in its mother's leisure moments. Later on, after the manner of young chickens, he was fed haphazard, according to circumstances and the will of fortune. The open space between the cottage and the high wall giving on the roadway served as stable and courtyard. He joined in the life of this enclosure as soon as he could crawl on all fours.

[10]

His father, returning from emigration with his fortune still unmade, had died some months before the child's birth, as animals and paupers die; of no known disease, for lack of physician; and without sorrow, for lack of preceding joy. He had left to his wife and aged mother the task of feeding, from the meagre yield of one stony plot, his six daughters and the child that was about to be born.

The fourteenth day after her travail, the woman was duly churched and the child baptized.

The village pope was a paunchy old man with a pimpled face, pouched and bloated by *robola* (a heavy Cephalonian wine), and almost lost in a flowing white beard. He plunged the child thrice into the font, covering his nose and ears with his heavy peasant fingers; and as the child, stifling and choking, emitted cries that the priest, an expert in the matter, considered exaggerated, the service was spiced with a sprinkling of the most uncanonical expletives.

When the ceremony was finished, he expressed the usual wish to the mother and grandmother that the child should "live to them"; and added: "the little nipper has got the devil in him," which concisely contradicted the rite he had just accomplished; but a Greek priest troubles his head little with theological subtleties. He makes the right gestures, blunders through the appointed prayers and reads the appropriate passages in the prescribed books, understands little enough of the Alexandrian Greek of the Gospel, and still less of the Byzantine Greek of the liturgy and canticles. As for the mystery of the grace of God, of the efficacy of the sacraments that he administers, he hardly boggles at the nature of them.

The child was baptized Ulysses, with the second name of George.

The Greek instinct wants to lose neither the renown of the fine flower of her history, nor the favour of the great mediators of the orthodox paradise. The name of a hero protected of old by the gods of Olympus linked with that of an influential saint close to the actual divinity seems the best assurance against the slings and arrows of fortune, from whatever quarter they may come. Armed with such names a child will be better equipped to fight his way along the tortuous footpaths of life.

Ulysses spent his first years crawling, running, and somersaulting about his mother's courtyard. He lived close to the ground, rolling in the offal of goats. His sisters worked afield, his mother tended the poultry, and his grandmother busied herself with everything and nothing. Sometimes she poked the fire, which never seemed to kindle, and she was always knitting a stocking which rarely became a pair. On Sunday they went to Mass and ate a hot dish of beans cooked in oil. During the rest of the week a loaf of bread, a handful of olives, and sometimes a hard goat-milk cheese sufficed for the whole family. This minimum of life was enough for the women; for the mother and grandmother from experience, for the daughters from atavism. Their horizon was limited by the high walls that surrounded them. The words, "It is the will of God," explained every misfortune: plague among the chickens or the loss of a son or a husband. The words, "May God help us," held all the share of energy that they believed themselves authorized to exert. Bounded by these two interjectional prayers, life flowed by, quiet, chaste, and miserable. Greater activity would have compromised their standing in the village.

Ulysses, in the depth of his young male consciousness, was already growing restless. Sometimes he escaped into the road to be dragged back with boxes on the ear that varied only in their source. Usually it was one of his sisters, sometimes his mother, more rarely his grandmother, who rendered him this service. Moreover, all these feminine clouts on the head did him no great harm. He howled a little on principle and as a precaution, but chiefly to satisfy his elders and to flatter them.

This was his first contact with life. Life, he felt, consisted mainly of received or avoided blows, and in this his precocious philosophy was not far wrong. He learned to avoid them early, without being tempted to give them back. He was ripening visibly to that bitter struggle that has no mercy on the weak, and in which only the most cunning and alert resignation has some chance of success.

The life of the Greek, in his own land, is a hard and

thankless one. He has to outwit, in a lunatic competition of enormous appetites and miserable resources, the churlish drought of his native soil and the hundred hazards of his stormy island seas. So the best among them go away; and in emigration, the Greek is forced to fling himself against hermetically sealed communities, against unjust and humiliating barriers. He must insinuate himself through closed doors, and acquire an esteem which is always denied to him. He must accustom himself to all trades, all circumstances, and all climates. These conditions drive him to a certain fatalistic opportunism. The "Good Hour" explains all his successes, and the "Evil Hour" all his rebuffs. Between these two Hours he can, without malevolence, be overweening with the humble and, without shame, humble with the overweening. It is sufficient to avoid his equals, for from them there is nothing to be gained, and always to attempt the exploitation of those who are either above or below him.

For Ulysses, the "Good Hour" was the clout avoided, and the "Evil Hour" the clout received. In these blows, coming as they did without explanation, and in a cycle that was automatic, but lacking in any commensurable rhythm, he soon realized the existence of a blind destiny whose arm no one can escape but whom one could, perhaps, outwit.

Later, when he was sent to the village school, the family clout made way for the schoolmaster's clout, which was heavier and more frequent. It was mainly through his kick-reddened little backside that his A.B.C. penetrated his skull. It was cemented there by slaps on the right cheek or on the left, regulated by some mysterious antiphony, to be interrupted only by the double slap on both cheeks at once.

Ulysses learned nothing useful at school. Sixty-one little urchins, crammed to stifling point in a narrow, unventilated room (for the schoolmaster dreaded catching cold more than the reek of sixty-one little bodies that had never in their lives been washed, except by their own sweat), shouted at the top of their voices endless strings of mutilated words whose meaning was never explained to them. During the two years that he went to school the only thing that he learned was one clear and indisputable truth: that everything has at least two names—the Romaic or vulgar name and the classical or noble one. He already knew that egg was called αὐγό; he now learned that it should be called ᾠόν. When he repeated this word to his grandmother, she told him not to be an impertinent little brat. In church, he had already heard the priest and the lay-reader speaking an incomprehensible Greek; at school, he learned the Lord's Prayer. He learned that, although he used the word ψωμί when he asked his mother for bread, he had to use the word αρτος when he asked his Heavenly Father to give him his. As he sometimes received an additional slice of bread from his mother, but never once saw the bread of his Maker, he came to the conclusion that perhaps it was an im-

[15]

aginary, ethereal bread, a symbol. He was not long in understanding, like the rest of his compatriots, that the usual word is the only one that can obtain a useful end, whereas only the classical word can uplift you to the regions of pure thought. The result is that the world of ideas and that of everyday needs are definitely divorced. Expressed in different words, these two worlds never meet, each held prisoner in its own inescapable mould. Needs, and their expression, live, evolve, and adapt themselves to ambient necessity. Ideas, slaves to their immutable expression, remain outside the sphere of workaday life. The needs are perhaps vulgar, but they are sober and clear, while the realm of ideas will always be sublime, stiff, and unyielding. To express them the Greek must struggle with formulas created in the time of Pericles, for which he will always have a superstitious admiration, but never that affectionate intimacy which alone can bear fruit. His stereotyped philosophy remains fossilized and barren; but his wants are burning. All that he expresses in everyday language—the virtues of the olive, the oil with its dash of rancidity, fried meats and their acrid fumes—he will never forget. His devotion to his mother and sisters can push him to martyrdom, for feelings lie also in the realm of simple speech, but he will boast grandiloquently of liberty, equality, and fraternity, which are spoken of in the classic tongue, ready to betray them at the earliest opportunity. The political game being played in literary Greek, he will

[16]

never be able to sacrifice himself for a political idea. He talks of it for the pleasure of fashioning pompous periods for which only the subtlest dialectic is propitious; but there the game stops. As long as the Greeks have two languages they will all let themselves be killed for a need, or a feeling, but never for an idea.

But this classical, ethereal language, floating far above all daily contingencies, has its use. It generates ambition.

With his little playmates, in the presence of his incomprehensible schoolmaster, Ulysses soon became aware of a higher region behind the cryptic words. And, as one always stretches out one's hand towards a beckoning mystery, they strove towards this supremacy that was so hard to attain; it was a land to be conquered, a glory to be achieved. The irrepressible arrivism of the Greek thrives on such words. In them he sees the illusion of a less sordid state of life, they egg him on towards high adventure. For one, this will be a university degree, for another, riches. Ulysses pursued the illusion of gold. The wonderful metal had been manifested to him only in the opulent gums of an old fellow-townsman returned from America, for the fortunes of emigrant Greeks are always represented by the number of their gold teeth. When Ulysses spoke about it to his grandmother, she said:

"God grant that one day you come back with teeth like that!"

So, with greedy ears, he followed the dazzling nomenclatures of his schoolmaster, and secretly began to sell to the village money-lender's son eggs filched from his mother's hen roost. But, more important than everything else, he learned of the profit to be reaped by flattering and bribing the mighty. He learned to acquire good marks and to escape well-deserved punishment by offering his teacher a bunch of flowers picked in the meadows or, on the great holidays, a young pullet that his mother believed lost or stolen.

Definition forming the essence of Greek instruction, Ulysses very soon realized all its imperfections. Everyday experience proved to him that the definite never precisely adheres to the words that are supposed to circumscribe it, and that this partly excuses untruth and the accurate, but useful, half-truth. He would already swear on the slightest provocation by all the lives that were dear to him and, above all, by "the Saint"—Gerasymos being understood.

He was armed for the fray. He broached the subject to his mother.

"Mother," he said one evening, "I can read and write; aren't you tired of feeding me?"

"I tired of it long ago," replied the poor woman.

"I am going away," replied Ulysses.

"Go towards the Good!" concluded his mother.

This dialogue, worthy of Sparta, was carried no further. The departure of men in Greece is the common lot.

[18]

The next morning, he kissed his mother, his grand-mother, and his six sisters. His mother and grand-mother made the sign of the cross upon him, gave him a loaf of bread and a handful of olives, and he set out. Barefoot, clad in short, tattered knickerbockers held up by a single brace running bandolier-wise over his right shoulder and across a collarless shirt of coarse linen patterned with little squares of grey and white, he wended his way downhill towards Argostoli, the port of Cephalonia. He arrived there at nightfall and slept on the quay.

At dawn the next day he got one of his little com-rades to explain the secrets of boot-blacking to him. As a little boot-black had just died, leaving no heir, Ulysses inherited his box and brushes. The first day he blacked six pairs of boots and went to sleep that night with sixty lepta in his pocket. This proved to be his usual income.

As it was summer time, he filled his leisure hours by learning to swim. With his little friends he jumped off the quay into water that was black with all the harbour rubbish, and retrieved everything that gleamed from the coagulate slime at the bottom: sardine tins, frag-ments of anchor-chain, and sometimes big lumps of coal that had fallen from some passing steamer.

Buyers were to be found for all these things. Such was the misery in Greece at that time that a serviceable utensil would be made out of an old tin, or a few links of anchor-chain would be used as ballast for a fishing net. A good lump of English coal chipped to pieces with the minute precision of a chemist lasted two long months for the rare occasions when the kitchen fire was kindled. In the ports where this scavenging was profitable, all the little urchins became passionate devotees, preparing themselves by dives of a few feet for the enormous depths attained by the sponge-fishermen. Ulysses sometimes gained as much as ten drachmas a day. As fortune favours the bold, he soon had a real stroke of good luck.

The British Mediterranean fleet had just concentrated in the bay of Argostoli. Having seen the glitter of English gold and silver on the quays and in the taverns, Ulysses felt that these blue jackets and red tunics were, for little Greek boys, a visible incarnation of Providence. For slight services as tavern guide, or buyer of their tobacco and cigarette papers, he was given big English coins, which he was told were worth twice as much as the Greek drachmas. He learned that the copper ones were called "pennis," and the silver ones that the sailors flung upon the tavern counters, "selinia," in the Anglo-Greek jargon of the ports.

Every day he swam out to the British fleet and howled: "Pennis! pennis! pennis!" till he was hoarse, and large copper pieces would tumble from the towers of those floating castles. Ulysses caught them as he swam and kept them in his mouth till he almost choked. He swallowed one or two. They were never lost. Delving minutely, he found them again when they had reached their last destination.

Sometimes the officers threw him a piece of silver. He lost none of these, as they reflected the sun better than the copper, and, as he cleft the water, Ulysses murmured: "May God preserve them!" confounding, in his consciousness muddled by the rush of the blue-green waters, the giver and the gift. Returning from the fleet, Ulysses would make a collection of all those objects that float around a British fleet at anchor: loaves of bread, empty boxes, big pieces of cheese, and, above all, empty bottles—hundreds of empty bottles floating hither and thither at the mercy of the wind and the waves. He herded all these oddments before him, drove them like a flock of sheep, and ran to sell them in the town as soon as he reached the shore. After three days, competition became unbridled. All the little guttersnipes of Argostoli swam for hours around the fleet. The fleet itself had never engaged in such desperate battles as those of the little Greeks that lived on the crumbs of British opulence. The game was no longer worth the swimming and diving, and Ulysses retired from business.

He had amassed eleven selinia, forty-eight pennis, and more than forty drachmas from the sale of his floatsam. He ran to share the fruits of his activity with his mother. He was actuated just as much by filial love as by the adventurer's professional pride.

"I'll show her what I can do," he said to himself.

[21]

When she saw his fortune, his mother cried:

"Eh, the little brigand! He's sharp enough to nail a horseshoe onto a fly!"

His grandmother, more detached from the things of this world, hearing, more than understanding, the tale Ulysses told, crossed herself and declared:

"A mad pope baptized him!" the priest's madness being considered contagious through the baptismal water, a token of success for the child baptized.

After passing one night under his mother's roof the little adventurer set off for the town once more, lightened of half his fortune; but that which remained to him still exceeded all his early hopes.

When the British fleet weighed anchor, Argostoli seemed very empty and poor. Already he had begun to dream of vaster, richer, more populous horizons. Athens attracted him. He had heard that they gave ten lepta there for cleaning a pair of shoes, instead of the little coin that his fellow-townsmen paid. For several months he had tried all the boats. He would go on board, black several pairs of boots, and ask permission to continue his work during the journey, and was regularly chased off with kicks when the moment for weighing anchor came.

Desperate, he began to fear that he would end his days in Argostoli, having never reached the Eldorado of his childhood's dreams. He gnawed at his halter. He would have walked to Athens, were he not held captive on an island.

In the end, however, he disembarked at Piræus as a first-class passenger. The monthly boat had just dropped anchor. He climbed aboard and, finding her almost empty, cleaned only two pairs of shoes. He was free to explore the inside of the boat and, wandering down the corridors, he saw that the first-class cabins were locked. A servant, half asleep in the heat of the afternoon, was awakened by the grating of a door-knob that Ulysses had tried to turn, and Ulysses was chased onto the deck under a shower of cuffs and curses. There, a huge sailor, who was drawing in the gang-plank, at the end of his breath and his stock of male-dictions, took up the servant's parable. With one last kick Ulysses was hurled over the scuppers onto the steps of the gang-plank. On the last rung, before throwing himself into the water, he regained his balance with a tumbling and clattering of bottles and brushes. When he had re-collected his entire stock-in-trade, he discovered that the last step of the gang-plank had been raised almost level with a porthole. The porthole was open. Between the long drop into the darkness—it was already night—and the round port-hole in its frame of glittering brass, harbinger of well-being and a voyage under the most luxurious condi-tions, Ulysses did not hesitate. First he stretched out his left arm, at the end of which his precious box was dangling, then seized the porthole-frame with his right hand, and insinuated his head and shoulders. As he was only seven, and in no wise stout from his daily diet of a slice of bread and half a dozen olives, he just managed to get through. With the noiseless sinuosity of a kitten, he balanced himself skilfully, threw his box onto a bunk inside, and succeeded in drawing in his two bare legs, which were still kicking outside the boat when she was already under way.

Nobody came to disturb the peace of his first voyage.

He went through some terrible moments at Patras. The calm of his solitude was shattered by the din of shifting cargo, the hubbub of flustered passengers, and the shouting of the boatmen.

Already he could see himself being flung into the waters of an unknown port, swimming like a dolphin towards distant Cephalonia. It terrified him to look out of his porthole at those unfamiliar waves, against which he would probably have to pit his strength. But soon the first turns of the screw reassured him, and he fell to nibbling a little crust of bread. It was his first and last meal during the voyage. All of a sudden he heard the lock rasping, and, inside, the door-knob began to turn, half round to the left, then to the right. This happened several times. He could already feel the agony of the stripes that awaited him, for there was no escape. The vessel was far out to sea. But the alarm lasted only a few seconds, and the door remained shut. One of the stewards had just been polishing the door handle, but on the outside only, as it happened to be under the eye of the officers, for a Greek servant never performs an obviously useless task. The brass inside the cabin could grow green with verdigris, as long as the visible part was polished enough to avoid an immediate reproach or a fine. This moderation, this sober and just measure in domestic service, proved to be the salvation of Ulysses.

At Piræus, he thought the boat was sinking. Howls, oaths, and violent impacts gave him the impression of a general free-for-all fight for safety. He opened the porthole and prepared to hurl himself to death or deliverance. To spy out his escape, he put out his head as far as his eyes, so as to see without being seen. He had just time to dodge a grappling iron thrown by an expert hand to hook onto the porthole-rim, and just escaped having his temples smashed in. Luckily, it was only a boat that had moored onto the ship while it was still going at full speed, the better to receive the first passengers. This way of boarding boats with full steam ahead is peculiar to Greek boatmen. They come almost exclusively from the Mahi district, and from Cape Matapan, which, of old, supplied Greece with her boldest pirates. Their descendants console themselves, in these sad times, by pursuing passengers as they come to port and boarding vessels in this strange fashion, not so much to haggle over their clients as to preserve their old form, keeping their hands in till the dawn of better days, when the heroic boarding of vessels on the high seas will again be possible.

Death, so narrowly avoided, was the agent of

Ulysses' salvation. Squirming painfully through the porthole (as the hook took up most of the room), Ulysses slid into the boat, down the rope that was stretched to breaking point by the speed of the vessel, before the astonished eyes of the boatman. He was received by an angry fist that flung him into the bottom of the boat. "That's a fine face for a first-class passenger!" the fist shouted, atremble with rage. Ulysses, bruised, and shaking with fright, splashing about in the bilge-water that rolled in the bottom of the boat, began to sob.

"What harm have I done you?" he pleaded.

"What harm have you done me?" bellowed the boatman, standing in the bows. "I'll soon teach you what harm you have done me."

Ulysses learned, in a few moments of ear-splitting invective, all his newly attributed vices, and his father's, and his mother's, and those of his remotest ancestors. The boatman ended with a resounding threat:

"I'll spit you alive, you spawn of a Turk!"

The silent old greybeard who held the tiller and managed, more or less, to avoid the ship and lessen the number of collisions with the other boats that formed an entire convoy in tow, took pity on him.

"The child's right. What harm has he done us?" he said.

"What harm?" the boatman answered. "He takes up the room that some respectable person would have paid for, some rich man, with trunks and suitcases!"

"I'll pay you too!" cried Ulysses proudly. "Look!"

From a little purse of coarse linen he drew a handful of copper and silver coins. At sight of this, the forward-standing boatman's fury returned. But this time his anger was tempered with a certain goodwill. Straddling in the prow, with one hand on the towline, he flung the palm of the other, with its five fingers spread, towards the sad face of Ulysses, making that venerable Greek gesture of opprobrium which is always accompanied by the exclamation, "There!"

"Na!" he cried. "Do you think I am going to take money off you? You! Na!" and this became the subject of further maledictory amplification.

"Look at that face! Is that barefoot little boot-black, that *lustro*, that filthy little guttersnipe with the milk still running out of his nostrils, going to pay *me? Me?*" the boatman grunted.

Ulysses caught his first glimpse of hope in this excess of indignity. Quickly, very quickly, he retied the string of his little purse.

2

THE important question of the cleaning of boots by little *lustros* has never been sufficiently studied. The Greek savants who reconstruct the Parthenon, patiently rebuild the history of Hellenism, make and unmake a hundred times the syntax of one Pindaric verse, discover that Napoleon, and nearly all great men, were of Greek origin, or unfurl the scroll of illustrious but complex genealogies to glorify some family that is cock of the social walk, have completely forgotten the walk itself, and its principal glory: the little Athenian *lustro*.

No one knows when and how this industry began. It is known to have closely followed the importation of the first pair of European shoes. It is thought to have already been exercised on the *tsarouchi*, the national red leather shoes. Nothing more is known. But, besides this, the *lustro* has always been known in Greece as the only swift and faithful messenger. The letter, or the sum of money, which is entrusted to him, reaches its destination with irreproachable security and speed, and the excellence of this method still prevails over telegraph and telephone and the government postal service. No progress has succeeded in laying siege to this ancient institution.

But the mystery of its origin remains, and is complicated by a further incomprehensible detail. All the *lustros* come from Megalopolis, a large market town in the Peloponnese, and they form an exclusive guild with an implacable legal code. The brotherhood has its own tenets and its own scheme of justice, and enjoys a complete monopoly, whether ratified by law or not. How can this predestination and privilege be explained?

All unwittingly, Ulysses became its victim. Being a Cephalonian, he was forbidden to ply his trade. He could do it only on the sly, in the suburbs and outlying districts after dark, when surveillance was slackened. So pitilessly was he hunted and so recurrent and painful were the stripes that he received, that he no longer knew where to lay his head. His life was one of continual injury. His boot-blacking box was upset, the letters entrusted to him were seized. Neither could he avail himself of the night-shelters, and other advantages, of the brotherhood. Every one of his little workfellows could bully him as he pleased. One day he complained to a policeman, who said:

"If you don't come from Megalopolis, what can I do for you? Look for another trade."

It was easily said, but not so easily done, as boot-cleaning is by far the best profession for little urchins.

No matter how great the competition, the demand is always greater than the supply, as the cleanliness of his footgear is a constant anxiety to the Athenian. He can be poor, with patched clothes and shoes in tatters, but the tattered shoes must shine. In the blinding dust of summer, and on rainy winter days when the streets of Athens are turned to quagmires, he has his boots cleaned every three or four hours. He can endure anything—hunger, thirst, and misery—but his feet must glitter. Is this yearning of historical origin? The winged sandals of Hermes, the fleet foot of Achilles, and a hundred other legends clearly show that all down the ages the Greek world has attached a primordial importance to feet. Could it be the token of a race of travellers and runners, the most celebrated of whom—Pheidippides, the runner of Marathon who brought the tidings of victory—died when he realized that he had forgotten to brush the dust from his sandals before entering the Stadium?

So great is the part played by feet in the history and legend of Greece that it is not groundless to believe that the Athenian predilection for brilliant footgear springs from some ancient law, deep-rooted and ineluctable.

Ulysses was not slow to realize that the confraternity of *lustros* would make it impossible for him to stay in the capital. His earnings dwindled from day to day. He was already delving into his slender capital. The Evil Hour pursued him. Only once did he meet the Good

[30]

Hour. But when it came, its results were manifold.

It was raining in torrents, and the roads had soon become rivers. To cross from one pavement to the other, one had to wade through deep water. Ulysses, frozen and shivering, took shelter under the eaves of a penthouse, brushing the boots of passers-by whose journey was almost finished and who did not wish to reach their home, shop, or office in such a plight. The rain had cleared the streets of its accustomed *lustros*, so, for one or two hours, he had the field to himself. But soon a lurking *lustro*, doing duty as a scout, fell upon his tracks, and he had to take flight and hide his box. Chance brought him close to a timbermaster's yard, and, seeing that forest of planks, Ulysses had a flash of genius.

Leaving his boot-blacking box as a pledge, he succeeded in borrowing the longest plank, two smaller ones, and four solid blocks, and these he dragged to the most-frequented crossing in the street, and made a bridge there. Two of the blocks served as supports, and he laid the ends of the two short planks on either pavement, and linked them with the longest. Planting himself ankle-deep in the water in the middle of the street, he levied a toll. He asked only one lepton per head, and so great was the service he performed that his customers sometimes gave him two, while for families he accepted a reduced inclusive fee; and no one denied him his well-earned obol. The Greek avoids all legal or official impositions with horror, but always respects a precarious and improvised right, above all if he senses that it is backed by a subtle idea.

By the grace of God, or that of Jupiter the Rain-Giver, the downpour lasted for two days and a night. Ulysses, drenched and sleepless, never budged from his post, and when fair weather broke through again, he returned the planks to the timbermaster and redeemed his boot-blacking box. His idea had earned him more than forty drachmas. It was riches, and he could return to Cephalonia and face his mother with his head held high.

Some municipal elections were in progress at that time, and six candidates were fighting for the glory of becoming Mayor of Athens, and Ulysses was hired six times, at three lepta the time, to swell the number of adherents of each of the candidates. For the Athenian *lustros* form the great core of electoral following.

It is not unfair to say that their incomprehensible acclamations, their windmill gestures, and their piercing weathercock cries represent the opinion of the electorate and the sovereignty of the masses faithfully enough.

As it rarely rains in Athens, and as elections are of frequent but not of daily occurrence, and as he was forbidden to ply his trade, he determined to return to the fold before choosing some more propitious emigration. He haunted the quays of the Piræus, waiting for the arrival of some ship bound for Argostoli.

One evening he was called into a coffee-house to

black the boots of a large man with grizzling hair and cheeks the colour of sun-scorched hide. For a coffee-house Greek, he was oddly silent. Sea-folk talk little, even in that sonorous Greece that has chattered, pro-pounded, and discussed for more than thirty centuries without ever achieving the slightest harmony. The clientele of the coffee-house consisted of sponge-fishermen who came there to smoke their nargilehs and play *préfa*. In the engulfing cloud of thick smoke, the only things to be heard were the bubbling of the nargilehs and the smack of the cards, flung upon the table by muscular fists that had been hardened by the labour of oar and rope. Every face bore the sea's marks: the reddened skin, furrowed by premature wrinkles and seared by the salt spray; the features frozen in a grimace, from the glare that tortured their blinking eyes, screwed up to pierce the fog and the dazzling light. Sponge-fishers bear the impress of the sea deeper graved upon them than any other sailors. For sailors endure the rigours only of the surface, but the sponge-fishers, those of all that lies beneath. At the huge pressures they encounter, the sea wrings them cruelly, and they absorb the salt through all their pores, they become one with her. Sad amphibians, they are not slow to show the stigmata of their calling. About the squalid rickety tables were grouped men who had grown old before their time, crippled or paralysed in the dayspring of their youth. A knotted and powerful hand held the cards it was also forced to play, while

[33]

the other, white and bloodless, hung in terrible uselessness. From time to time a player made his bid in signs, to players whose eyes were aghast with the agony of the dumb, or full of the eternal questioning of the deaf. In another part of the room a young man, whose every movement betrayed the strength and perfection of his body, could follow the game only by lowering to the level of the table his one short-sighted eye, the other being already lost. From a young Apollo with the smile of a child, a shark had carried away a leg below the knee. Still being able to swim, he continued his trade till some vital mutilation should quite disqualify him.

All these men bore the mark of active, uncomplaining resignation, defying the fate they had suffered and which they were doomed to suffer. Ulysses felt no dismay at the martyrdom that surrounded him.

"Captain," he said, leaning over the biggest pair of boots that he had ever blacked, "where are you bound for?"

"What has that got to do with you, young snotnose?" asked the man of the sea. "I work the Egyptian coasts and you don't even know where that is."

"Take me with you," said Ulysses.

"What should I do with a little shepherd boy like you?" (Greek sailors bestow this title on all landsmen.)

"I don't come from the mainland," answered Ulysses, "I am from the islands. I'm a Cephalonian!"

"I thought you came from Megalopolis, being a *lustro*. But tell me, since when has Cephalonia turned out sailors?"

For the seafaring Greek only the island from which he himself hails is capable of producing worthy sons. But as each island despises all the others, they enjoy an equitable return of compliments.

Ulysses, who already knew how to push himself forward by boasting, answered without raising his head:

"We had a heavy storm, coming from Cephalonia; I didn't get sea-sick."

"You came on a steamer?" asked the captain.

Ulysses had to admit it.

"And since when," continued the old man, "has a steamer been a fit craft for a sailor?"

This paradox was fraught with all the Greek sailor's disdain for engine and propeller. Oar and sail alone enjoy a certain esteem. But when the boat lies becalmed and the sail hangs like a rag, or when she is tossed by the storm and the canvas is in shreds, and the oars are useless, they both become, despite the respect they enjoy, objects of endless calumny.

"Cursed things," they shout, "only the machine is blessed by God!"

Sailors of all countries have similar contradictions, insult and praise following each other to suit the opportunity.

"Take me," said Ulysses again; "you won't regret it."

"Listen, little shepherd boy, I command a sponge-

[35]

fishing boat, a little thing like that—" He made a gesture. "You would perish with fright, out there between the sky and the sea! And you don't even know how to dive."

Here Ulysses could assert himself without lying. "I? Why, at Argostoli I used to dive two fathoms deep to pick up coins."

At these words the captain burst out laughing so violently that he upset Ulysses' box and silenced the whole coffee-house.

"Listen, boys," he cried to the company, "put down your cards and stop talking. This little shepherd brat here wants me to take him on as a sponge-fisher, because he says he can dive two fathoms."

In this café, full of men of the sea and especially of sponge-fishers, Ulysses' words brought the house down. They laid aside their cards and the supple coils of their nargilehs, and the whole room was shaken by titanic laughter, slow in dying. Each one of them shouted his opinion of Ulysses' diving.

"Here's good health to you, my two-fathom sponge-fisher!"

"This really *is* a diver at last!"

"That's a strange thing too—a sponge-fisher from Cephalonia!"

"Perhaps he has discovered a new bed of sponges at two fathoms!"

"His mother's milk is still running out of his nose, and he thinks it is the blood flowing out of his ears!"

[36]

For all these men, tossed by the storm, impregnated through and through with the salt water they absorbed at the enormous pressures of twenty or forty fathoms down, where it was their bitter task to search for sponges in the darkness of the deep and of their own terrifying solitude, which was broken only by the sombre bulk of some shark swimming overhead, and from which they returned choking, and red with the blood that ran from all their pores, Ulysses' boasted prowess was of the richest comedy.

Ulysses kept his head in the whirlwind of laughter and derision that he had let loose. Firmly planted with his two little legs far apart, holding his box under his left arm, his right fist clamped to his hip and his head held high, he cried to all those heroes of the blue-green waters:

"What are you laughing at me for? Didn't you all start at one or two fathoms? If, later on, you reached the forty fathoms you talk so much about, by the Saint! I'll reach them quicker and better than any of you."

Ulysses' attitude pleased the company. The cards were picked up and the nargilehs began bubbling again.

An old diver came up to him and said:

"I don't know what to make of you, you young scamp. You've got the devil in you. I've got my papers and everything is ready. We sail as soon as there is an off-shore wind."

He moved away, and Ulysses followed him. The boat looked very small. She was soundly built and all decked over, with an enormous single lateen sail, manned by divers from the island of Hydra. There were eight of them.

When Ulysses and the captain went on board, they were all asleep.

"Take this blanket and doss down over there," the captain told him.

Ulysses was soon fast asleep with his boot-blacking box as pillow. When he awoke, the sun was high and they were well out to sea near Ægina, for they had cast off without breaking his deep child's sleep. The vessel was heading for the open sea, sailing an easy eight knots. She soon rounded Hydra, her home port, and the cradle of the whole crew. At the moment when they lost sight of the white blur that marked the only town and the little port of the island, the captain rose from the rudder and made the sign of the cross.

"Shield us with thy protection, St. Constantine of Hydra!"

"Shield us with thy protection," answered the whole crew, standing and crossing itself.

"Shield us with thy protection, Chryssospiliotissa," said the captain again.

"Shield us with thy protection," answered the crew in unison.

It was the Virgin of the Golden Grotto, whose name was the vessel's also.

[38]

"As we've got a Cephalonian on board, let him invoke the saint of his island," added the captain.

"Shield us with thy protection, St. Gerasymos of Cephalonia!" piped Ulysses, making the sign of the cross. "Shield us with thy protection!" repeated the Hydriotes.

Strong in her manifold protection, the boat sailed on for two days and two nights under the same wind.

On the horizon they could just see the highest mountains of Crete, swimming like a low, blue-shaded cloud, almost invisible. Soon it was sea, nothing but sea, mistress of the horizon, swept clean of all earthly blemish; the all-powerful sea against which there is no appeal. The sight of land, however far off it be, bears for the sailor an appearance of protection, illusive perhaps, and often treacherous, but always consolatory. In his battle against the waves he sees in each little black speck, in the slightest suspicion of a rock, a solid body independent of the storm; and his heart finds support there, and hardens itself for the conflict. As soon as he loses sight of it, nothing remains but the few boards below him, so many prisoners, slaves of the element which bears them at its will, flings them to the sky, and draws them back into the hollow of its waves, to the mingled chorus of the winds' howling, the hallucinating undertone of the waves, the creaking of the ropes, and the groaning of torn ship's timbers, weighted down and tortured by the buffets of the waters, pitiless, contradictory, and murderous. The sea is an immense striving, seemingly aware and infinitely cruel, of dislocation, of victory, and of annihilation.

As with all novices, all that Ulysses felt was the satisfaction of newness. For he knew nothing of the way they followed, nor of their destination, their dangers, and their hopes. His companions, with the silence of men who know each other too well, attended to constant little duties whose utility was nowise apparent. He was taught to fold his blanket. He helped scrub the deck. He realized that only a minute and scrupulous orderliness made the life of so many men in such a small place possible. When the waves grew wilder, Ulysses felt sea-sick.

"To leeward!" they shouted and, not at all understanding this expression, and overcome by a violent retching, he sullied the cleanliness of the deck to windward.

"Get a bucket and clean it up!" ordered the captain.

Staggering, and grasping at anything for support, he lay on his stomach and lowered the bucket into the water. As the boat was travelling at great speed, the jerk of the filled bucket strained the rope, and Ulysses let go.

"That shows the good of taking a snivelling little landsman aboard!" the master-diver shouted to the captain. "Now we'll have to fetch up a sponge, just to pay for the bucket."

"Hold your tongue!" answered the captain. "He'll learn!"

"Yes, and before he learns, we'll be ruined by all the damages he'll cost us!"

"As far as the matter in hand goes, a bucket more or less makes no difference," answered the captain. "It's enough for me to take on a fresh hand just for you to become his enemy."

The race of sponge-fishers is a hard one to handle. Servants of a pitiless trade, they are without pity. Often they are escaped jail-birds who never dare to land, and their ship is their only refuge against the police and indiscreet questioning. Unable to follow any human livelihood, all that is left to them to earn their bread is the deserted barbarian coasts, and the desolate soundings of the high seas. Their life is an endless struggle with death. On the surface they fight against the waves, and in the depths, against sharks, against suffocation, and against the paralysis brought on by the terrible pressures they endure, when, weighted with a heavy stone, they descend ever further and further down, even to forty fathoms deep. The sponge once plucked, they leave their stone, and rebound to the surface. Such is the pressure with which they remount to the boat, that they are flung several yards into the air, to fall into the water again like bleeding phantoms, drawn on board almost inanimate, sweating blood through all their pores, convulsed and panting. This is the cost of the soft sponge that we use so thoughtlessly, and the sanguinary price is always paid by the miserable Greeks who have the sad monop-

[41]

oly of this accursed trade. At this livelihood, death comes early. In the eyes of divers, who bear upon them the mark of death, the lives of others are worthless. A knife-thrust follows the smallest altercation, and to command such men, one must have been one of them, and proven stronger and braver than one's fellows. Nothing must be overlooked. Like the tamer of wild beasts, he who would lead them must, with his own hands, violently avenge the smallest disrespect or disobedience. If the captain lets himself "take the air," as the Greek expression has it, he is lost. Anarchy reigns on board.

As contraband is not unknown in the sponge-fishing trade, often being, in fact, its corollary, all these revolts against a life of superhuman hardship are aggravated by the cupidity unleashed by a fruitful and illicit commerce. Care must be taken to guard against profitable informing, and against calumnies arising from the division of the profits. The shares having been allotted beforehand, they must be strictly followed out, and the proof of the fairness of the division be shown beyond question.

But whatever the vices and crimes of these human beings in whom so little humanity survives, much will be pardoned to them; for they have suffered much, and if they are found deserving of hell, they will have had their punishment in this world, and, above all, in its seas.

[42]

Such was the galley in which Ulysses had set sail. The crossing, soon hindered by contrary winds, lasted more than eleven days. They passed through nerve-shattering calms and furious clouts of wind. The calm provoked childish quarrels about nothing: a piece of bread, or an article of tackle out of place. But the storm united them all against the common foe, the instinct of the sailor being stronger than the anger of the man.

Ulysses, miserable, inexpert, and lost amid this world of unloosed forces, ended up by praying for foul weather. He was less frightened of that than of the shouts, the oaths, and the blows with which these brutes would menace each other. He had nothing to complain of, however, for all the scanty tenderness that still tarried at the bottom of those hard hearts was his, and in their churlish, thorny fashion, too strong to be sweet, his comrades cherished him. They gave him the corner that was best sheltered from the wind and spray to sleep in. Sometimes these attentions assumed an intimacy that some vague instinct bade him shun. A few words exchanged between the captain and the master-diver in undertones, but unstripped of their hatred, had seemed equivocal to him. His surroundings, what he already knew of them, and what he suspected, aroused his caution. Among those beings, all cast in the same steely mould, he felt he was an exception and, as such, an enviable object. In those eyes,

[43]

dulled by the over-long struggle and by sights that were over-fraught with horror, he thought that he could sometimes discern the gleam of a longing.

These few days spent between the two pitiless elements—the sea and the unbridled passions of men—had ripened his thought and supplied his heart with strength.

3

✵✵✵✵✵✵✵✵✵✵✵✵✵✵✵✵✵✵✵✵✵✵✵✵✵✵✵✵✵✵✵✵✵✵✵✵✵✵✵

ALEXANDRIA has never really left off being a Greek town. The large commerce and the small are both still in the hands of the sons of wing-footed Hermes.

In the heart of the native quarter, the grocer Dimitri kept a sordid but profitable shop. A few boxes of macaroni, some sacks of rice and potatoes, and one or two casks of olives and herrings completed his modest fortune; to which must be added some bills signed by the natives of the quarter, half of them representing capital that he had loaned and half the interest that was owed to him. He himself owed nothing to anyone.

He had started business by signing a bill to pay the rent of his stall. He stocked it with goods bought on credit at the large *bakal* in the Rue Sherif. But for years now he had been paying cash, and had only to wait for the goods to be delivered. He was greatly helped by his dealings in hashish, which he kept hidden in the room behind his shop and passed on to coffee-house keepers, for the use of their hashashin.

For several months now he had been assisted by young Ulysses, whom he had made the "son of his soul." This relationship is peculiar to the Greeks. It consists of taking a child into service, until he grows up and takes flight. The "soul son" has the right to food and shelter, provided that he behaves himself. The "soul father" tries to set the child up in life when he is of riper years, and, if it is a girl, to marry her off. Legal adoption is rare, but happens now and then.

So there was our Ulysses, firmly established as "soul son" of the good *bakal* Dimitri in the city founded by Alexander the Great—the Iskanderieh of the fellahin, who, proud of the illustrious founder, still link his name to that of their town and look on his fellow-countrymen with affectionate indulgence.

Near the end of the voyage, Ulysses had understood that the services demanded of him, though quite usual in the sponge-fishing trade, had only a very obscure link with the trade itself. He had understood too that he owed a lot to the fierce rivalry of the ship's captain and the master-diver, and in particular a superabundance of provisions and lighter work. Above all, he had understood full well that sponge-fishing was only the pretext, the subsidiary reason, of the voyage, while the obvious, immediate reason was the unloading of a cargo of hashish that lay carefully hidden beneath the hull and the interior planking. In this mass of impressions and concrete revelations he fancied that he

[46]

glimpsed a continuous chain of future possibilities, over which he pondered deeply all through his last day at sea while the ship lay becalmed, with flapping sails, in full sight of a low-lying coast that never seemed to get any nearer.

As soon as the anchor had touched bottom in the bay of Marsa-Matroukh, the Egyptian coastguard came on board to verify the ship's papers, which were in perfect order, and to examine the hold, whose inextricable disarray displayed the intricacies of the finest art. He poked in every corner of the little boat. He sounded each timber, each plank, and finding the resonance to his taste, the faithful coastguard received the classic baksheesh, and went ashore.

As young Ulysses was a novice, no one looked on him with distrust; he happened to hear the coastguard whisper a mysterious word to the captain—"*Aghamos*," which in Greek means "bachelor," "unmarried." As such a confidence seemed to have no immediate meaning, he deemed it wise to keep the three syllables in mind.

For two days the boat lay at anchor, which they weighed only when a strong westerly wind seemed to put all ideas of sponge-fishing out of the question. After losing sight of land, they tacked eastwards again, keeping close to the shore. Night found the boat anchored in front of a ruined fortress. A few planks were pulled up and the landing of the hashish began. Ulysses noticed that there was nobody there to receive it.

They stacked the whole cargo in a little crevice in the rock at the fortress's foot and sealed the hole with a heavy boulder.

The precious merchandise was now on Egyptian soil, and the captain put on his Sunday clothes and prepared to land. Ulysses asked to go with him, complaining of sea-sickness and expressing a longing to be on solid earth again. The master-diver opposed his demand, so the captain consented. They almost came to blows, but in the end Ulysses accompanied the captain, who had a tryst with his Alexandrian clients. After a few hours' march, they reached the Attarin quarter. Passing in front of a Greek shop, Ulysses suddenly recognized the sickly reek of hashish.

The plot hatched in sight of Marsa-Matroukh was put into sudden action. Ulysses, slipping away from the captain's side in the crowd, ran into the shop and crouched behind the counter before the astonished eyes of the proprietor.

"What are you up to, you little ragamuffin?"

"Hide me till it is dark, and your fortune is made!" whispered Ulysses.

The Greek is a gambler; he is attracted by the mysteries of chance. Dimitri the *bakal* learned from Ulysses where the hashish was hidden. The word *Aghamos*, opportunely remembered and repeated, suggested to the grocer the fort of Aghami, by the entrance of Alexandria port. They immediately went and changed the hiding place, and the captain, little dis-

[48]

posed to tarry on Egyptian soil to warn the police of Ulysses' desertion, never saw either his apprentice or his hashish again.

Thus it was that Ulysses became Dimitri's "soul son." His tasks, which he faithfully fulfilled for three years, lay in opening the shop in the morning, cleaning and shaking the barrels and sacks, preventing the dust from settling, helping his master to sell his wares from dawn to dark, and shutting up shop after the latter had gone home for the night. He slept on two potato sacks, which he arranged side by side on the ground, engulfed by the stillness of the night, unlighted by lamp or candle, and disturbed only by the rats that scuttled and nibbled among the wares. At dawn he was awakened by the buzzing and teasing of a cloud of those Egyptian house flies, daring, sticky, boisterous, and heroic.

But the part he played in Dimitri's business soon began to tell. Always giving just measure in weighing, he had the art of tying up parcels; he swept behind the counter a portion of each piece of goods that he sold—more strictly speaking, its tithe. Towards evening the drawer was filled with dozens of olives, potatoes, and broken bits of macaroni, and a thick layer of rice, dried peas, and beans and other odds and ends. Cheese being more difficult to steal, he delivered it accurately, except for the ground parmesan, little heaps of which filled the drawer with its acrid smell.

Thanks to Ulysses, the deals in hashish were made

[49]

with greater regularity and safety. He suggested that they should deliver the groceries at the purchaser's house. At first Dimitri was against it. But when Ulysses explained that, if they got in a stock of paper bags, they could fill the bottom of each one of them with hashish, and supply the precious stuff to the hashish fiends and a parcel of olives to the honest housewife simultaneously, Dimitri began to open his eyes to the genius of his "soul son."

At this revelation Dimitri, who was little given to eloquence as a rule, told Ulysses in demotic Greek that he was "the devil's own stocking," which, in the Greek lower middle class, from the Balkan peaks to Cape Matapan, and from Corfu to Smyrna, is the highest tribute that can be paid, expressing symbolically the speed and astuteness which are the very soul of commerce. In pure Greek, "the winged sandal of Hermes" would have been more apt, though the symbol is the same, like the spirit of Greece, which from the time of Hermes to that of Dimitri has changed but little. But, as it was a question of success in smuggling and the grocery line, Dimitri, out of respect for the language of Homer, contented himself with the baser idiom.

A year before, the success of Ulysses had moved his employer to give him, unsolicited, a rise in wages. On his own initiative, he began to pay him a pound a month. Madame Dimitri—Kyria Lenio—with whom the question had long been mooted, found it unnecessary, and even dangerous. True to the words in the Gospel: "Ask, and it shall be given you," she found it irreverent to give without the asking; besides, she thought that money was pernicious for the young. Struck by these two peremptory arguments, Dimitri made a compromise with his conscience, with his helpmeet, and with Holy Writ. Ulysses' appointment held good, but he resolved never to give him his monthly pound. Every month he bought him a savings stamp of the National Bank of Greece, but looked after it himself. So Ulysses was immune from all the dangers to which a young man with pocket-money is exposed, and Dimitri, following the Gospel, accorded to the Hellenic Government, as proxy for Ulysses, a loan, which is always in demand.

Although she regretted the solution, Kyria Lenio could find nothing to say against it. She consoled herself by calling Ulysses a "παλιόπαιδο," a guttersnipe, and prophesied his damnation in this world and the next.

Like many wives whose husbands prosper in business, she feared first of all the "Eye"—the evil one— and, secondly, any particularly skilful collaborator. She tried to save her husband by a series of dire prophecies that she denied when all was well, and started again and confirmed as soon as trouble appeared; thus managing, like all women, to be always in the right. Despite these mental restrictions, she would display, on feast days, the tenderness of a mother to Ulysses. From the first, he had partaken of the Easter lamb with his masters, likewise the unleavened bread of the first Monday in Lent. On the feast days of St. George, St. Helen, and St. Dimitrios, respectively, she presented him with three *loucoumadès*—buns soaked in honey and oil. The rest of the time she looked on him with the eyes of an inquisitor. She never let him come near her house, lest he should seduce the servant girl, and each time that she came to the grocery, she found some excuse to scold him for possible, perhaps probable, but, at all events, not actual, misdeeds. She countered all her husband's reproaches with the remark that "it would do him good."

It did him harm. Feeling that, in spite of everything, his employers did not trust him, he fell to wondering whether their trust was worth the earning. The Greek, born astute, is disarmed by blind confidence. As soon as he feels the vaguest doubt, the slightest watchfulness, the most nebulous control, he tries to overcome it. He will never take advantage of an open door, but he will pick the lock of a safe.

The prophetic calumnies of Kyria Lenio drew Ulysses' attention to the paradoxical presence, in the shop, of a safe whose key had never been entrusted to him. When he was alone at night, he wondered whether it was fair and logical that the money he had earned for his master during the day should be locked up so carefully; against him, as he was the only person who stayed at the shop at night.

What would there have been in this safe had he not

[52]

worked with all his might, using all the resources of his intelligence? What had his master been earning before his arrival? All the district knew, and told him, that his custom had become at least three times as large. Ulysses knew that the profits had increased thanks to his skill and his little paper bags ballasted with hashish. What was the use of all that silver and gold asleep in the safe, when he knew that, if he had the handling of it, the coins would go spinning on fruitful errands which he could see without being quite able to specify? Would he always have to juggle with olives, macaroni, and rice, and never with their jingling counterpart? At night, especially in those long summer nights when the late-watching flies kept him awake with their malevolent skirmishing, these fancies haunted him. During the day, when the safe opened at his master's touch, he found himself watching the lock. He let himself be caught by the spell of the shifting tumblers, and it all seemed very solid and complicated, but much less subtly organized than his own brain. He imagined all sorts of locks and how he could force them. Theft? It never even entered his head. To him theft was the last, and perhaps the only, resource of the incapable. Inside him he felt the slow movement of energies that excluded theft. But to lend himself the money that he needed to extend his operations, to offer himself the provender that his otherwise unnourishable appetite for action hungered after, seemed very legitimate. To remain a little grocer's cat, or to travel the world in

[53]

quest of great things? Whenever he had made a suggestion, had not Dimitri dubbed him "μεγαλοπραγμων," doer of great things? How could he do great things without the money that lay in the hands of the catchpenny Barba Dimitri, who could see no further than his nose? Once, when he had learned from a customer that cotton had fallen heavily, lower than ever before, had he not advised Barba Dimitri to buy? He had been irritated by his master's futile answer:

"Cotton is for the islanders, and the mountaineers on the slopes of Pelion, not for us Moreans. The Morea turns out grocers, not cotton merchants," with which Barba Dimitri had crossed himself, crying: "Behind me, Satan!" to rout temptation and send the tempter packing.

One day, as it was very hot, and there were no customers, Ulysses leant on the counter and said to his master, who was half asleep on a stool by the doorstep:

"Barba Dimitri, how much money has mounted up for me?"

"Mind your own business. I give it and I look after it," answered his master.

Ulysses thought it best to push the question no further that day. But his business instinct made his thoughts coincide with the old adage in Roman law: "Giving and keeping is without value." In that case keeping became theft. Set a thief to catch a thief! But he came to no definite conclusion.

For many long months he went on serving the customers, keeping shop, watching the safe, and turning
over in his mind many subtle and burning questions
that contradicted each other at the very moment that
they came to agreement, before he brought up again
the question of his promotion and of his forced economy.

This time he tackled the subject in the affirmative:

"Barba Dimitri, it's two years now that you have
been giving me a pound a month. So now I've got
twenty-four pounds."

"Do you want to get twenty-four stripes where you
sit down?" answered Barba Dimitri.

"Whose money is it?" Ulysses insisted.

"Yours, while you are with me," said Barba Dimitri
coldly.

This answer of Barba Dimitri had two meanings.
It meant that he was the guardian of the money, but
also it meant slavery, the continuation of service, the
putting out of action of Ulysses beside the old *bakal*.
Ulysses murmured, with a threatening hint in his
voice:

"Perhaps it would be better if it were yours but
looked after by me."

"Hold your tongue! Can't you see I am reading the
paper?" the grocer shouted. Ulysses realized that it was
not the time to insist.

The daily paper being among Greeks a highly respected institution, one would no sooner think of in-

[55]

terrupting anyone who was reading it than one would interrupt the priest at the altar or a mother suckling her child. Through his paper, the Greek is in communion with the great Idea, with the reconquest of Constantinople, with his ancestors of the time of Pericles, with the Prime Minister, and he will be delighted or enraged according to the whim of the broadsheet, or his political party. It is read in a low voice, each letter being formed with the lips. If it is read out loud, it is intoned and declaimed like a great classic or the Epistle of St. Paul at Mass. Stress is laid on all the proper names, which are pompously maimed or distorted. The newspaper is respected in inverse ratio to the depth with which it is understood, and direct statement is treated with scorn unless it insults the opposite party. The voice grows, the neck-veins swell, the forehead is bathed with a light sweat that sets the spectacles slipping on the nose, breaking the period at its outset. When he reads his paper, every Greek becomes and feels an orator and a statesman. He does not read to learn, as he knows everything beforehand. He reads to imagine himself in Parliament, at the Palace, attending a cabinet meeting in St. James's, at the Quai d'Orsay. With Disraeli he refutes Gorchakov, with Alexander II he frees the serfs, with Delyanni he routs Tricoupis, or the other way, according to the time and feeling. With King Constantine he marries the sister of Kaiser Wilhelm, and then wishes to remain neutral for family reasons; with Condouriotes he sinks the Turkish fleet; with Averoff he reconstructs the Stadium; with Polites he edifies the temple of international law; with MacDonald he turns all the ironclads into floating chapels of peace; with Hoover he swims in oceans of dollar bills; with Venizelos he looks at everything through rose-coloured glasses, even Greek finance; with Condyles he rides in triumph through Macedonia; with King George he lands at Piræus; and with Eden he travels from Moscow to Warsaw, from Warsaw to Berlin, and from Berlin to Geneva.

Through his paper the Greek becomes exaggerated, metamorphosed, and transcendental; the most squalid stall becomes a palace, the smallest dinghy a transatlantic liner, a dirty cap a crown imperial, and a rickety stool a throne. The counter is turned into a seat in Parliament, whence he inspires armies to victory, explains defeats, concludes alliances; invests Mussolini with the aspirations of Nero, the Pope with the desire to annihilate Orthodoxy, and Venizelos, even after his death, with the most contradictory, mysterious, staggering, criminal, or holy activities, according to the evolution of events. The newspaper is an enchantment and a mystery. Having read his paper, the Greek reads nothing else; which costs less and, in the long run, does less harm.

So Barba Dimitri read his paper and Ulysses held

his peace, letting his own affairs recede before the great speech of Tricoupis on the twelve provisories and the interruption of Coumoundouros on the bridge of the Alpheus.

4

✿✿✿

FOR some time Ulysses was drawn from his customary musings by an unwonted event. Almost every week he bore a supply of hashish to a stews where several of the best clients could not to the full enjoy the pleasures which the house offered without the help of this powerful aphrodisiac. Usually, he saw only an old black hag who opened the door, and the mistress of the house, a mass of quivering fat in dragging slippers, her left eye projecting while the right seemed irredeemably lost behind an eyelid too heavy for lifting, with rings on her fingers almost invisible in the flesh that swelled up around them. Her fat hung in loose folds, and when she walked, with her arms spread out like the points of a compass, and her legs apart to keep her tottering balance, it all rocked and rolled with a twofold movement, simultaneously vertical and circular.

Ulysses, although he was already eighteen, was still of a chastity as whole as it was unguessed at. Apart from the advances of the sponge-fishers, of which he had had only an inkling, no sexual influence had ever troubled it. He often visited the house without ever wondering what happened there. He was even offered coffee by the old black besom, without becoming vaguely aware of the atmosphere of ambient debauchery. His was the chastity of the Greek whose every sense is absorbed by business or that of beasts out of their season.

One evening, while he was passing the time of day over a coffee that the old black hag had offered him, a young Negro girl came and sat down beside them. The British rule, which had just established itself in Egypt, had suppressed slavery, filling the houses of ill renown with Negresses. The poor girls were turned out of doors by the pashas, who wanted slaves, and no free and salaried domestics. So the British police had emptied the family harems to fill the harems of prostitution; European morality often has these contradictory effects when it is unthinkingly imposed on differently organized communities. However, this moralistic measure was full of unforeseen consequences for Ulysses. He soon found himself being led by the hand into a room where everything that met his eye astonished him. Having always slept on two potato sacks on the ground, in the back room of Dimitri's shop, he was amazed to see a bed bigger than the back room itself, and so soft that, when he tried it, he almost lost his balance. He wondered at the mirror, where he saw himself full length for the first time, a tall, slim, but solid young man; at the undreamed-of wash basin, he always having swilled his face in the morning at the public fountain in the Rue Attarin. He marvelled at other instruments with odd shapes at whose uses he did not even try to guess. He was still more astonished to find himself naked, beside a naked woman whose black skin had the air of a chaste apparel. Above all was he amazed to feel himself helped to perform new gestures which certainly amused him, but only very slightly, while the black form which clung to his seemed tortured by a delirium as spasmodic and clamorous as it was inexplicable. He could find only one possible explanation: that the Negroes have "the Belief of the Horned One," which links them with devils, with libidinous rams, sons of the god Pan, of whose name and ways he knew nothing. The same game having been often repeated, he reaped a very slender pleasure from it, and a deep weariness; so much so that he spent the whole night away from the shop for the first time, sleep having overcome him as he lay. After that, he seldom slept on his two potato sacks, finding the bed of his Negress softer and more comfortable, and this softness was the greatest pleasure that he found there. The rest seemed to be the preliminary ransom of good sleep. But, little by little, he gathered considerable advantages from this place that was frequented by so many different types of people. He became, in a way, of the house. He sold much more

[61]

hashish than before. He learned a few words of Sudanese from his Negress, translated into Arabic, which he already spoke fluently. From his meetings with British sergeants who visited the establishment, he picked up the essential words of their sober tongue. From the confidences of drunken soldiers, he learned of General Baker's plan to reconquer the Sudan. The thirsty soldiers were condemned to follow him into regions which they cursed because they would not be able to find whisky and beer in them. The Negress talked of her country, which she had never seen, having been born in an Egyptian harem, but of which her mother had told her. Gradually, Ulysses' horizon broadened. He filled in as best he could the gaps in his education, and he was quick to profit by whatever opportunities the house offered him. He made great strides, well tutored in the school of primordial gestures. He even taught a great lesson himself. The Negress, being occupied one evening, left him to a Greek comrade-in-arms, called Eudoxia. On entering the bedchamber of his countrywoman, he was enchanted to see an icon of St. George, his patron saint, on the wall. Before getting into bed, Eudoxia made the sign of the cross before the icon, and he eagerly followed her example, making a reverence before the knight who pranced on horseback above the prostrate dragon.

He let the Greek have her will with him, as he had done with the Negress. But when, on a thoughtless impulse, she made an unaccustomed approach, he at first understood nothing; he only found it ridiculous. But when he realized its purpose, he leapt out of bed and spat in her face.

"Whore!" he cried. "May your communion be damned! Doing what you have done with the same lips that have drunk the blood of Christ!"

Twenty centuries of latent Orthodoxy protested through the mouth of Ulysses so forcefully, that twenty centuries of Orthodoxy imposed themselves upon the smirched soul of the Greek girl. And beneath the astonished eyes of St. George and the blazing eyes of the dragon in its death throes, the lost woman fell on her knees, crossing herself a thousand times, and dashing her forehead upon the floor.

"Forgive me," she said, to St. George, doubtless. "Forgive me, I knew not what I did!"

Ulysses left her at her repentance, which, in the Orthodox Church, means falling on one's knees and striking one's forehead against the ground, then standing up and making the sign of the cross, to begin once more, continuing in accordance with the gravity of the sin.

This theological scene was soon all round the house. All the Greek girls learned Ulysses' lesson from Eudoxia, and, with a similar reaction, they all showed their contrition, and thenceforward refused all practices which they believed irreverent.

Several clients complained to the enraged housebawd. She soon put everything to rights, after having commented in a few varied and well-chosen oaths on the eucharistic susceptibilities of her Greek inmates, dubbing Ulysses, the Patriarch of Alexandria, and all his monkish crew, catamites. To the married popes she expressed the extenuating remark that they were only cuckolds. Then she consigned the whole breed of priests and all the saints of heaven to the last outrages. It must be said in her favour that the house-bawd was the daughter of one of Garibaldi's lieutenants, and that she hated the Pope. Never having received the sacrament, she could but ill understand the eucharistic scruples of her Orthodox flock; and, being a Neapolitan, she possessed thoroughly only that part of the noble Greek tongue which is devoted to invective and which, since the time of Aristophanes, mainly exploits the private parts and their immediate neighbourhood, with the diverse abuses to which they may be put. She ended by forbidding Ulysses the house. He had, as a matter of fact, little temptation to return, his only regret being its luxurious sleeping accommodations.

In this manner Ulysses' love life came to an end. No moral stain, debauched habit, or hallucinating visions lingered in his mind. On the contrary, his adventures proved of service to him. He had become acquainted with a British sergeant-major behind the brothel's welcoming doors. After his tenth bottle of stout the soldier always became garrulous. The sergeant-major had spoken to him of the expedition into the Sudan, and had informed him that Suakin would be the concentration point of the troops. He had also said that should Ulysses set up a licensed grocery there as a canteen for the thirsty and too severely rationed soldiers, it would be a profitable concern. The sergeant, who had taken part in the Zulu campaign, told him that a Greek had made his fortune there in this way. He advised Ulysses to take at least a hundred pounds' worth of beer, whisky, and gin, and above all an apparatus for making soda-water, indispensable to the officers. The sergeant-major, dead drunk, had often kissed Ulysses, promising his protection. One day, when he was a little less drunk than usual, he even demanded a quarter-share in the takings. Ulysses later understood that this was meant as a great favour and a sure token of help.

A few nights after he had begun sleeping again on Barba Dimitri's two potato sacks, Ulysses' couch was softened by the gilded dreams that the British sergeant-major had set aturning in his head.

Of the brothel, the Negress, and Eudoxia, only a blurred memory remained. All he could see was the fat sergeant-major and his unquenchable thirst. He worked out what such a thirst, multiplied by two or three thousand—the strength of the British column—would bring in daily, at so much the big glass and so much the small. Being ill versed in written calculation, his wits were swift and accurate. On the one hand he juggled with piastres and banas, and on the other with okas and drams. After several minutes that would have aroused the jealousy of Euclid and Einstein, he came to a decision. Suakin was already his adopted country. He could already see his stall crammed with soldiers full of the contents of his bottles, and his pockets full of the contents of theirs.

The sergeant-major had promised to indicate the moment of his departure and to facilitate the journey. Without neglecting his clients, Ulysses served them with the amiable lackadaisy of a servant who has been given a week's notice. With Barba Dimitri he had unconsciously assumed the airs and graces of his future superiority. He answered the recriminations of Kyria Lenio with a smiling and detached silence. Everything that he now did had the stamp of the provisional. He suggested no more grandiose ideas to his master, who accordingly fell back into his wonted serenity. Barba Dimitri could read his paper without fear of interruption. Certainly, the daily profits showed a tendency to decrease, and the daily receipts were no longer so monumental, but peace reigned in the shop. There was no longer that atmosphere of unrest that haunts the surroundings of the ambitious. The store-keeper revelled in this calm, and Ulysses revelled in the thought of his next act. But still the sergeant-major did not come; he would come without doubt when the time was ripe; the quarter-share was the best security. But if he failed to appear at all, Ulysses could get to Suakin alone. He did not need the Englishman to open up his shop. The English had only to drink and Ulysses had only to fill their glasses. And fill them he would from morning till night and from night till morning. When he is earning, the Greek is tireless, his resistance knows no bounds, and it is when he begins to lose that his moral resistance can be seen. Being both fatalistic and optimistic, he never loses his head, and believes that the Good Hour follows the Evil Hour, without the reverse's seeming inevitable. But hereditary influence was what most attracted Ulysses to Suakin. To exploit the natives of every country is for the Greek an atavistic dream, the brilliance of whose glitter grows in ratio to its inaccessibility. The races that dwell on the Mediterranean shores attract him less than do their fellows on the shores of the Indian or Atlantic Oceans. He prefers either the quite black or the quite white. Those shades of colour nearer his own are certainly not to be sneezed at, but they interest him less. The Frank has a very appetizing reputation in Greece. The κουτο φραγκος—the stupid Frank—has become so well known that this composite word is inseparable from the language of every day. Among the Franks, the highest place is given to the Englishman; he is thought to be more κοὐτός—more stupid—richer, and, above all, more generous, than the rest. After the Englishman comes, or rather came, the Russian. The Italian has always had a bad press; the Frenchman is judged a mediocre client. Apart from the Franks, the Turk was considered as full of possibilities, but apt to turn dangerous. With the Egyptian fellah one is on a better footing. The thing that had instinctively attracted Ulysses in the Suakin expedition was the fusion, the coincidence of the Negro and the Englishman. The idea of exploiting these two extremes of colour simultaneously enchanted him. Buying from the Negro to sell to the Englishman seemed the ideal form of commerce. He was well versed in all the secrets of barter. To barter elephants' tusks for mother-of-pearl buttons with the natives, to exchange them again among the palefaces for jingling guineas, seemed the one livelihood dreamed of by all his ancestors and realized only by the very chosen among them.

Why, then, was the sergeant-major so long in coming? But one evening he came when Barba Dimitri had left, as for this meeting, this final negotiation, it was necessary to be a long time alone and undisturbed. Knowing the ways of soldiers, and, above all, of English soldiers, Ulysses had carefully hidden in the store behind the shop several bottles of stout and one of a good brand of whisky. He had worked for them a whole month. All the gleanings in the drawer went to the sum that finally bought them. Every day olives, broken macaroni, and the dust of cheese and rice had been sold to buy the propitiatory libation. Ulysses forgave himself these petty larcenies, deciding that they were only his due, as before his time those morsels could only have fallen on the floor and been lost.

[68]

After the customary greetings between the civil and military—majestic rigidity on one side and dorsal suppleness on the other—there was a long silence while Ulysses uncorked two bottles of stout, which the sergeant-major, sweating from the summer heat and from the two bars that he had already looked in at, emptied almost without taking breath. After a few murmurs of approbation and thanks, which Ulysses accepted with a smile of excuse that he had not been able to do better, accompanied by a pleonasmatic gesture of both hands, a fresh silence fell while the soldier took off his braid-and-medal-garnished tunic, and undid two buttons of his shirt and the two buttons of his trousers that were most palpably irking his huge paunch. Ulysses had advised this unclothing, which puts a man off his guard, helping as best he could.

Now they could talk. And the Englishman talked at length: three words of Arabic and one word of English, each time pressed home by a heavy slap on Ulysses' back and a guffaw that dwindled into a hiccup, was the obligatory dialect for his exordium. Like all men who have a business mind, Ulysses knew how to listen. Like all fat men, the Englishman was prolix. He talked about the Zulu war, of the Greek storeman, of the commander-in-chief, of the dishonesty of his fellow-men, of his own perfect honesty, of his wife and children, of his scanty pay, of generals who had enriched themselves, of the greatness of the British Empire, and of the virtues of Queen Victoria. Hearing this name, which he had often heard the sergeant shouting when he was being turned out of the stews, Ulysses realized that his interlocutor was already fairly drunk and that the transaction was well launched. But he restrained his desire to press forward too fast. He deemed it best to keep the definite arrangements till after the seventh bottle, when the Englishman would be in perfect humour, and before the eighth, as he knew from experience that at this stage he capsized into complete unconsciousness. Between the seventh and eighth bottles he was sure to make a very favourable promise, which he would keep; while after the eighth the promise would certainly be more generous, but almost as certainly forgotten.

Ulysses' period with the Negress and Eudoxia in the most propitious surroundings for the study of human nature—when it was unmasked by venery or by drink —had equipped him with an excellent idea of physiological psychology. He had learned to gauge the effect of body on mind. He had observed that, under the sway of the inebriacy of the flesh, all those who paid in advance paid liberally and with goodwill, while there was always difficulty with those who paid afterwards. He had sworn to himself that, if he were ever in such a plight—which God forfend!—he would pay afterwards. Whereas under the sway of alcoholic drunkenness it was always best to present the bill at the end. From this he gleaned the knowledge that, in general, the body's thirst dwindled the more it was satisfied, and that alcoholic thirst waxed with fuel; and, in particular, that it was best to attack the Englishman seriously only after his seventh bottle. He was not slow in reaching it. The great moment was drawing near. Ulysses' plans were made. He had framed his approach a thousand times, and knew by heart the words that he was about to pronounce. He pronounced them.

"Me not money—me work. You money—not work. Me three-quarters—you one-quarter!"

This was not his last word. For he already possessed forty pounds in Barba Dimitri's keeping, and as the obligations of the National Bank had risen, he could get at least sixty for them.

The Englishman hiccuped rather than said that he could provide only twenty-five of the necessary hundred pounds. Ulysses assumed a heart-broken expression and repeated several times: "No good, no good!" and looked reflective, so that the Englishman implored him to find some makeshift, not to let the thing go, not to leave him, the father of a family, without this exceptional but necessary windfall. When Ulysses saw that the other had become almost suppliant, he assumed a charitable tone of voice. He declared that he would borrow seventy-five pounds, which he agreed to join to the Englishman's twenty-five. But, he said, the loan would cost him at least forty percent interest, and that he was forced, to his great regret, to reduce the sergeant's share, proposing to give him ten percent of the net profits. The sergeant claimed twenty percent, but came down to twelve percent at the eighth bottle. With a charitable gesture, Ulysses agreed. He repeated the contract:

"Ulysses seventy-five pound, sergeant twenty-five. Ulysses eighty-eight percent, sergeant twelve percent."

"All right! That's a bargain," said the Englishman.

Ulysses did not understand the second half of the phrase. But as the sergeant stretched out his hand to shake, without quoting another figure, Ulysses considered the matter settled.

Everything was agreed and clear. Ulysses' greatest pleasure lay in what the Englishman had not grasped, that he, Ulysses, would receive forty percent on a sum that he, Ulysses, would lend himself, while the Englishman's money being his own, there would be no interest to pay, and the Englishman's share would be reduced from twenty-five percent to twelve percent.

Ulysses had won a still more signal victory in this first important negotiation: the Englishman was already asleep over his tenth bottle, having given him the twenty-five pounds.

Now there were only two difficulties to overcome: to rid the shop of the Englishman before the arrival of his employer and to wrest from the latter's grasp the obligations of the National Bank of Greece.

Meanwhile, Ulysses lay down and went to sleep on a few potato sacks, murmuring: "May the Hour be Good."

His Hour at awakening was Evil. Were the Englishman's beer and snoring contagious? Although Ulysses had drunk nothing, he was still sound asleep long after sunrise. For the first time in years, Barba Dimitri found the door of the shop closed. Like everything new, this phenomenon seemed fraught with danger. He was about to knock, but stayed his hand, looking around. The road, although a little too empty for his liking, seemed normal enough. He scouted the idea of a crime as too different from his long experience. He came to the conclusion that there had been a theft—which was much more familiar, and in perfect conformity to his way of thinking. Anyway, he decided that it would be more prudent to wait the passing of a shaweesh—a policeman. But in Egypt, as everywhere else, and in spite of the British occupation, policemen are rarely to be found when they are wanted. Some anguish-breeding moments dragged past. That closed door, which he had always found open, augured a complete change in Barba Dimitri's life. He found it humiliating that he, a married and settled man, well known in the quarter, should find himself standing in the road before a door that refused to open.

But to crown his misgivings he suddenly heard a snore that was so resounding that it sounded like a death-rattle. The idea of a crime became so convincing that he went in quest of the shaweesh. When he had found him, he began to explain the strange circumstances of which he already felt himself the victim.

[73]

He exhausted all the possibilities. At each one, the shaweesh unctuously repeated: *"La samah Allah!"*— "May God prevent it!" This pious invocation accompanied the sonorous tread of the shaweesh and the stealthy tread of Barba Dimitri up to the still unopened door.

To the shaweesh's punch, the door replied with a light snore; to his kick with a louder snore; to the butt of his rifle, which nearly smashed the panel, with such a strange howling that the Egyptian soldier took to his heels and waited at a distance, his hand on the hilt of his bayonet. But the door remained shut, and once again silence fell. The shaweesh took heart, murmuring: *"Stamfurah el Azim!"* which represents, for the followers of Mohammed, the summit of astonishment. Barba Dimitri echoed the same feeling, crying: " Ἔγα χριστέ και παναγία!"—"Come, Christ and the Holy Virgin!"

It was Ulysses, waking with a start, who came at last. Failing to rouse the sergeant, he had decided to face —alone—the anger of Barba Dimitri, whose presence he divined beyond the door. Being reckless by nature, he opened it wide. Seeing the British soldier, the Egyptian soldier leapt to attention, and Barba Dimitri doffed his slouch hat to the ground with a sweeping gesture that Louis XV would have appreciated. These two gestures, or rather these two reflexes, are an admirable proof of the colonizing force of the English. The sergeant went on snoring, the shaweesh's hand

[74]

remained rigid against his tarboosh, and Barba Dimitri's hat on the ground. This gave Ulysses just the time he needed to see how the land lay, and to study his resources. He had gone to sleep haunted by the thought that he would never be able to extract the all-important papers from Barba Dimitri. To break the safe would be child's play, but the idea of simple robbery disgusted him profoundly. How could he quit Barba Dimitri, who had received and treated him as his own child, with a clean record, otherwise than by being dismissed? This solution seemed to him to contain all the politeness and gratitude that he could for the moment offer his benefactor. The meeting of the important British sergeant, of the severe Egyptian shaweesh, and of the good Barba Dimitri, at that particular place and time, truly seemed to be the Good Hour that he had begged of the Lord as he fell asleep the night before. From humble, his manner became proud. He roused the sergeant, and explained in English that Barba Dimitri refused to pay him his savings. He explained the same grievance to the shaweesh in Arabic. To Barba Dimitri he stated briskly that the intervention of the shaweesh had dishonoured him, that it made his life unbearable in the quarter, that he would never dare to show his face to the customers again, and that he was forced, much against his will, to insist that his account should be settled on the spot. Barba Dimitri, having always led the peaceful life of a placid merchant, lost his head. He called Ulysses all the names which the modern Greek of the people flings in the face of creditors when they come to collect their debts. But the British sergeant put a stop to all this coil by a "Goddam!" accompanied by such a blow on the counter that the whole shop was shaken, and along with it Barba Dimitri's conviction in the justice of his argument. So great is the prestige of the British Army everywhere, and especially in the countries that it occupies, that the shaweesh, the most humble but the most immediate representative of Egyptian justice, was immediately convinced of the truth of Ulysses' claim and commanded Barba Dimitri to disgorge there and then all that was sought of him. The condemned party found his conviction too summary, scandalously premature, and outrageously unjust; but without appeal, since it had the sanction of the British Army of Occupation. Had there been only the Egyptian shaweesh, Barba Dimitri would have immediately thought of the Greek Consulate and of the thousand devices that extricate even the humblest Greek from the clutches of the Egyptian police. But he realized that it would have been futile to oppose Queen Victoria, especially when she was represented by the fattest sergeant in her army. There was a parcel of hashish, too, in the back of the store, whose reek might at any moment set twitching the expert nostrils of the shaweesh, who seemed to be sniffing already in a way that boded no good. He left his hat on the ground, and with the palms of those hands that had been brandished so vehemently towards his judges, Barba Dimitri made the ancestral gesture of patience and imminent conciliation. With a tread that was heavy but not lacking in dignity, he went behind the counter and approached the safe. He opened it only a few inches, for it was not fitting that everyone should see what was inside, and withdrew a tightly trussed packet. When he saw the good man obeying so easily and without revolt, Ulysses suffered a twinge of remorse. Shutting the safe, and duly arranging the lock so that it could not be reopened without the key, Barba Dimitri walked straight towards Ulysses and handed him the parcel, invoking with his eyes the eternal witness of the soldiers. The Egyptian remained impassive and the Englishman nodded his head in approval.

Thus the fortune of Ulysses was handed to him with all solemnity. As soon as Ulysses had taken the packet, Barba Dimitri scorched him with a thunder-fraught glance and pointed to the door with a gesture that was immediately obeyed, accompanied by the wish, "Go towards the good!" a euphemy that often covers the most terrible of curses. Barba Dimitri bowed so low before the sergeant-major that the soldier was already far off when he straightened himself again. As for the shaweesh, he stayed behind to ask for a pinch of hash-ish, of which he had divined the presence in the back-shop long before. This little favour was granted without hesitation, less in payment for the trouble caused than as a precaution for the ever uncertain future.

[77]

Although the conduct of his "soul son" was odious in his eyes, Barba Dimitri, paradoxically resembling Calypso, "who could find no consolation for the departure of Ulysses," was aware of such a yawning and unexpected gap, that, having tried in vain to read his paper, he realized that the most important event in his life had just taken place. He shut up shop and went home. This unseasonable home-coming, without fellow during thirty years of married life, set an unhealthy curiosity stirring in the bosom of Kyria Lenio. She demanded to be told everything immediately. And the condemnation of Kyria Lenio fell upon and augmented those of the shaweesh and the sergeant-major. After cursing Ulysses and bitterly heaping upon him all those epithets which in the Greek tongue are unfavourably coupled with the child's birth and engendering, she taxed her husband with such tyranny and injustice toward an excellent apprentice that it was only human that Ulysses should have abandoned him. Barba Dimitri flung back at her that she had never quit scolding him for unforgivable weakness and the most absurd generosity with the little rascal, whose departure should logically be a good riddance. With the best faith on earth, Kyria Lenio reiterated her last assertions, peremptorily confuted all those that she had been repeating for years, and was finally and unassailably in the right, after the fashion of womankind in all similar or analogous circumstances.

5

✱✱

A T the advice of the sergeant-major, Ulysses began to collect as cheaply as he could all the supplies that he needed for his Sudanese enterprise. He bought the best, in order to make a start that would satisfy his customers. Later on, he would water the whisky, weaken the soda-water, and find a substitute for Bass and pale ale. He made an agreement with the best importer of English liquor, by which, when he had twice renewed his stock, paying cash, he would be allowed a credit of two hundred pounds; and, thanks to the sergeant-major's presence, he got a wholesale discount which was by no means usual for so small an order. It was all delivered in crates, ready for transport. Ulysses did not waver a moment between the ways of land and sea. He chose the sea, and on the sea, a sailing ship. There was a barque bound for Port Said, and he offered his services, which were accepted, to defray the cost of freightage. From Port Said he would reach the Red Sea overland or by the canal,

[79]

and at Suez he would be sure to find some sambouk that called at Suakin.

Ulysses cherished all the Greek's optimistic confidence in the sea. Although he was in a hurry—for he had to be at his destination when the troops arrived—he suffered no qualms as to the contrariness of wind or waves. He believed them both propitious to Hellenic enterprise. He had the blood of too many navigators in his veins to doubt it; every Greek is a sailor, by profession or necessity, or by atavism. Besides, all over the world, on the seas of every continent, a Greek is sure to find another Greek, to help him on his way. So, at Port Said, Ulysses found a Greek pilot of the Canal Company who consented to ship him and his wares as far as Suez. But he counselled secrecy, and schooled him in subterfuge in case of difficulty, because the pilot's action was strictly forbidden in the company's rules.

Landing at Suez, the pilot wished him the Good Hour with fervour, and Ulysses began hunting the quays for the expected sambouk, which was nowhere to be found.

The old pilot had advised him to distrust the captains of the sambouks and their crews likewise. He had painted them even darker than the hue of their own skins. They were a terrible breed, he said, all smugglers and pirates, capable of doing away with a passenger without a qualm if his cargo seemed worth the rifling.

This bad news was confirmed by the first compatriot he met—he happened to be a freight agent—who promised him, however, an immediate departure on a sambouk of the best standing, whose captain was an intimate friend of his and a man of the highest character. Haralambos, the shipping agent, had no hesitation in advising Ulysses to buy a revolver and a few hundred cartridges, which he could sell him cheaply. This advice set several strategic considerations turning in Ulysses' brain. He determined to arm himself with a revolver but, above all, with prudence. The memory still lingered, from his experience among the sponge-fishers, of the captain who always stayed astern and slept sitting, so that the slightest sound would rouse him. A certain inborn strategy showed him the advantage of living on board quite surrounded by his packing-cases, so that they could not be opened and so that, in dire straits, they could serve him as a rampart against his potential enemies.

Having gleaned every possible provision that fortune offered him, Ulysses quietly awaited the sambouk's arrival.

He waited eight days; for, east of Suez, uncertainty and delay are the masters of destiny. But when the sambouk appeared, it was desirable in his eyes. Ulysses could not but find that Haralambos had exaggerated his intimacy with the captain, who seemed never to have clapped eyes on him before, and who, despite the advances of the agent, persevered in the distant attitude of all true desert Arabs. As for the freight, the bargain was long in striking, although everything seemed to be in complete agreement on both sides. The expression, "As you wish!" bounced from the lips of the Greek to the lips of the Arab; as soon as a figure was quoted it seemed to please both parties, but with no other result than fuel for more controversy.

From time to time, Haralambos, in his quality of intermediary, would whisper in the ear of one of the parties words which were known to the other but which he was doubtless not meant to hear. For, east of Suez, business is above all a pastime and an art, purged of all the vulgar utilitarianism that soils and abridges it in the West. When Haralambos felt that the season was ripe for finishing, and to force the last reserves of the Arab, he imposed his mediation; he said in a solemn voice:

"Let us pray to the Prophet!" upon which the Arab turned towards Mecca, raised his hands heavenwards, and intoned the single and sacramental prayer of Islam: "In the name of Allah the Merciful, the Loving-Kind!" while Haralambos extracted of Ulysses his last concession. When the Arab had finished his prayer, he turned toward the two Greeks. With an august and conciliating gesture, Haralambos put the right hand of Ulysses into the Arab's right hand, and formulated the price. The Arab said: *"Istabene,"* an Italian word which sanctifies agreement in Arabic. Ulysses said:

"*Istabene.*" The "symphony"—the agreement—had been attained before God and man.

The loading of the cargo started on the spot. It was summer time, and Ulysses declared that, as the sambouk had no cabin, his packing-cases would serve him for shelter. He arranged some of them in the stern in a solid wall, forming a triangle with the poop netting, and the after-starboard netting. Round about, he propped cases that were left purposely unstable. He meant to sleep as little as possible, but always in the centre of this improvised bastion.

The Arabs, having never had a Greek on board before, had no glimmer of all the strategy that the arrangement contained. It seemed an idle fancy.

When they left the quay, Ulysses having judiciously helped to haul in the anchor and hoist the sail, the captain concluded that his passenger was not altogether a stranger to seacraft. He asked Ulysses if he had been a sailor. Ulysses declared that he had been a sponge-fisher, for he deemed that, in showing himself well versed in navigation, he ran less risk of being cast ashore before his destination. East of Suez, no precaution is superfluous.

The sambouk was already spinning briskly along under a nor'easterly breeze. The huge sail was the only cloud in the night sky, clearer than a European day. The captain, at the helm, intoned the lagging monody of the songs of Islam, accompanied by the crew in muted unison. Ulysses, for fear of falling asleep, joined to theirs his voice, less deeply pitched but skilled in the same subtle modulations, and the Arabs marvelled to find a Roumi who knew their songs. They could not know that the wailing lament of Persia, after having conquered Arabia, and, through the Turks, Byzantium, became so deeply implanted in the soul of Hellas that it rooted out the male cadence of the antique rhythms, substituting its soft and fleeting oriental modulations.

For five hundred years the Greeks have sung their dreams and longings to the Persian rhythms; and even their revolt against their oppressor has found tongue through their oppressor's voice. The song of the Klephtes who guarded the sacred flame of Greek independence upon the impregnable heights of Pindus or, in unconquerable Maina, cursed the Turk in the Turkish way. The Greek Church, having forgotten the Byzantine psalmody, continues, even after the flinging off of the yoke, to honour the God of the Nazarenes after the manner of the singers of Islam. To the ear, the basilica and the mosque are closely mingled, and, music being the essence of the soul, this union in melody is perhaps the reason why the Greek feels himself more at home in the Moslem Orient than elsewhere, though here he is surrounded by his enemies of several centuries' conflict.

Deeper than the spirit's or the body's revolt, is there a tryst where the souls that vibrate to the same music

[84]

meet? Is this community of sound deeper and stronger than historic hatred and intellectual strife? Rhythm has its reasons of which Reason knows nothing, holding in thrall the boundless heart of mankind, which is stronger welded or sundered by its songs than by its deeds.

In the dark sapphire night, deepened and mellowed by the eternal threnody of the East, and accompanied by the thundering waves and the sail's shuddering, the sambouk bore Ulysses towards his fate.

6

◊◊◊

THE sambouk glided over the open sea for five torrid days and five nights of enchantment. Ulysses,
through the atavistic diligence of seacraft, fell in with
the work of the crew, and helped in all the little tasks
of shipboard that, useless for the most part, occupy
the sailor's soul and hand during a long journey.
Whenever there was talk of shifting his packing-cases,
Ulysses opposed it with such a prolix refusal and with
such complicated reasoning that the Arabs, open to argument when it has a strong enough pantomimic back-
ing, let themselves be persuaded. The most perfect harmony reigned between the crew and their passenger,
and their homely goodwill augured well. One evening,
nevertheless, the sailors showed signs of unrest. Their
eyes, trained to the slightest shades and signs of the
Red Sea's surface, descried a light dust which had just
hidden the coast of Arabia. At once they abandoned
the natural languor and proverbial calm of Mohammed's followers. Their wonted silence gave way to gut-

tural shouts, and their grave voices were rent in piercing cries. The sombre emptiness of the limitless horizons was fraught with anguish.

Running hither and thither they all seemed to set about some task that had never before been attempted. Each one seized something, but never the thing he wanted. Anonymous commands, hurled from each one of them to all the rest, arrested each action at its outset and withheld each incipient gesture. The barque, which up to then had seemed manned by a crew of imperturbable caliphs, assumed a chaotic atmosphere, as if it were a cage of maddened apes. Some leapt into the hold, others clambered up the rigging; the nimblest found themselves suddenly astride the yardarm, whence they climbed down again immediately, with no apparent goal save that of motion. The captain, who, since setting sail, had seemed to cow men and elements with one dominating glance, preserving a haughty detachment, was lost in the hubbub that engulfed them all. Everyone bellowed into his face advice that sounded more like commands, which he sometimes even followed, screaming through his last shreds of dignity that he would do nothing of the sort. Everyone wanted to do his fellow's work at the same time. Confusion bred confusion, and suddenly the whole crew found themselves face to face at the foot of the mainmast. Their noisy toil seemed to be directed towards furling the sail, but all their efforts were vain. The sail would not budge. The wind was blowing up stronger, and the huge expanse of canvas now bellied out like a balloon, now tugged and flapped at the mainmast as if to break it in two. The Mussulmans fell to swearing like Christians. They committed to the devil everything they could lay their hands on, the coming dawn, and the faith of their shipmates likewise.

In this orgy of blasphemy no one perceived that, as they were all gathered at the mainmast, the helm was left to its own irresponsible reactions, and that the noble sambouk was revolving on her own tail. Ulysses, who from inborn prudence had calmly remained in the middle of his packing-cases, was the only one to take stock of this unusual fact. It seemed to him that, a ship's main purpose being to reach some port, she stood to lose everything by pitching about in the same place.

The logic of Socrates, to which it was impossible that he should be wholly a stranger, indicated to him that, being close to an untended rudder, he had better steer himself, so, leaping from his turret of English liquor, he grasped the tiller.

This gesture was in itself laden with great possibilities, but the gesture alone was not enough. Holding the tiller, Ulysses determined to get it to rights, but the choice of direction was difficult. The tiller being in the middle, he did not know whether to move it to, or from, him. He watched the sail and the efforts of the men, who, since his seizing of the helm, had become his crew. No sceptre can give such a feeling of power as the helm of a ship.

Instinctively, he flung an order, which the wind snatched from his lips, and whirled away. Between the two Arabian coasts, the disyllabic Greek word "σκατά," which signifies "ordure"—the English word rhymes with "pit"—gained mastery over the gale. Reassured by these two syllables, he tried to issue a second order, screaming the magic word "κερατάδεζ," which, in modern Greek, means "horned ones," "cuckolds," and qualifies anyone who has not given satisfaction, even though he be a bachelor; and the Arabian wind carried away this word. The first word is one that fortifies the Greek soul against death and surrender, and the second, one which upholds the feeling of conjugal honour, the race's deepest well of strength. Unburdened of these two words, Ulysses felt lighter, and ideas began to circulate in his mind. He felt that in thrusting the bar to the side on which the boat was leaning, he would exert a lever and fulcrum action, and that the boat would right herself. Without knowing it, he sailed into the wind, and did that which all his sea-faring ancestors had done before him. All at once his wonder-stricken eyes saw the violent but momentarily powerless sail flogging as if to make a last struggling effort of resistance against the hands that clutched at it. He watched the sail yield to their tugging and slide slowly, but ever more limply, along the yardarm. The sail had been conquered, hollowed, beaten down, and

[89]

lay powerless on the deck. It heaved a little as if in its death-rigour, then subsided, and lay defeated on the deck without a breath of air or a flutter.

Meanwhile a hurricane was blowing, and the breakers flung themselves against the prow with murderous violence. The sambouk's bowsprit pointed now to the heavens, now into the abyss.

The men still beat at the sail as if to dispatch an enemy already dead, rolling on top of one another. The spray splashed Ulysses' face at the helm, and the tiller leapt now this side now that. He had fallen flat on his face in an unsuccessful effort to keep the tiller in line with the keel, by jamming his feet against the bulwarks. First it would deal him a savage blow in the chest, then drag him after it helplessly. . . .

He slid into the bilge-water, which was thick with mud and all the unnamed filth that breeds spontaneously in the bottoms of small sailing boats, and especially of sambouks. Realizing the hopelessness of all his efforts, he regained his feet with a bound. Clamping his outstretched hands into the stays of the poop rigging, he bestrode the tiller and, gripping it with both his legs, seemed master of the situation. The tiller's blows battered his shanks, but he somehow managed to get it under control, and felt a new access of strength from being on his two feet. Like all men in a sovereign but precarious position, he bellowed inarticulate words of command. It was mostly to reassure himself, to overcome his own fright by reassuring his shipmates. He shouted to them that they must wait till all the reefs were sheeted before hoisting sail. He did not understand their answer, but knew that his orders would be obeyed. In due season the sail slowly remounted the mainmast. After flogging a thousand times with a noise like giant slaps, the wind caught it fairly. Ulysses at the helm was lord of the hour; but the hour was short. As soon as the Arabs saw that the sambouk was no longer in immediate danger, the consciousness of their dignity, and of the distance that lay between the isolated Giaour and true believers, returned. The captain was the first to come to himself, to regain his assurance. Seizing the tiller from Ulysses, he bade him keep his place with a wave of his hand.

Ulysses fell to husbanding his bastion, which the gale had set atrembling, but which still held firm. He heard the Arabs discussing the Nazarene, which is an evil omen throughout Islam. He was not long in gathering that they held him guilty of inciting the storm and the sail's resistance, which had almost shipwrecked them. They were chiding him for the wind that still howled, and the jagged, foam-crested coral reefs that lay about them, and he felt his aloneness keenly. He feared neither wave nor reef; the Islamic menace seemed more imminent and more dire. One sailor even spat in his direction. A boisterous blast of wind drove the sambouk into a deep wave-trough, half submerging her for a few minutes. The Arabs, busy with fresh shouting, forgot their oaths against the Nazarene,

[91]

but Ulysses did not forget the Arabs. He profited by their disarray to load his revolver, which he laid out on top of a crate, along with the cartridge belt and its hundred rounds. When it was calmer again, they beheld Ulysses standing up behind his rampart, calling down all the curses of heaven upon their heads. He spoke to them of the sworn faith, of the sanctity of the Blessed Host, of his handling of the rudder without which they would all have perished, and of the coincidence, prompted by the heavenly powers, of their spitting and the last buffet of wind. As they did not seem convinced, he covered them with his revolver. Feeling that they were overcome, he bade them call upon the Prophet and, turning his back upon them, he bowed towards starboard and Mecca and intoned the first words of the prayer: "In the name of Allah the Merciful, the Loving-Kind . . ." The Arabs took up the hallowed words in their turn, and he held his peace, wishing to thrust his burgeoning apostasy no further than the just measure which assured his immediate security.

The praises of Allah had calmed the crew, and Ulysses felt himself less threatened by the men and more by the sea. The sambouk, driven by the wild wind, gambolled crazily over the waves, and already the hostile roar of the reefs that lay off the Egyptian coast could be heard in the distance.

The sambouk fled before the wind and plunged into the night, quite black by now. In answer to one of

Ulysses' questions, the captain pronounced the password of Islam: "*Kismet*"—"It is Destiny." When he
sought an answer that was less vague, Ulysses had to
content himself with the password of Mecca: "*Mek-
toub*"—"It is written." He understood that it was per-
chance written in the book of Allah that the sambouk
that bore him should be shattered on the coral reefs
that were roaring ever louder, boisterous and unseen;
and he resolved to give the lie to the Book of Life.
Fatalism is often useful, but it is not the essential
quality of a seafaring man. The sea delights in rape.
She is always hard to overcome, and sometimes she
will surrender herself only to the most daring, stubborn, and variable of enterprises. Ulysses realized that
in the hands of the crew the sambouk was heading for
destruction, which he deemed, from every point of
view, premature. To drown before twenty, or be dashed
to atoms on the reefs, when he had just acquired a
hundred pounds' worth of the rarest merchandise,
which he could sell at a good profit, seemed bad business. At one moment he saw himself being devoured
by a shark, and at the next, enthroned in a grocer's
shop, aswarm with customers, in the Rue Sherif. This
second vision, so much more attractive than the first,
engendered a plan. Aware of the crew's enmity, he
dared not suggest that he should be entrusted with the
rudder. He feared that the slightest initiative might
release a fury too great to be quenched by prayer. The
menace of his revolver did not seem to be bearing

[93]

fruit, and the same gestures rarely succeed if they are used too often, especially when they follow too close on each other's heels. He decided to adopt new and contradictory tactics. After piety and threat, he judged it best to flaunt ungodly and delicious temptations before their eyes. With a quick movement he split open a case of whisky. Uncorking a bottle, he took a pull at it and handed it to the captain, who nearly drained the rest. A good Mussulman is one who never pays for a drop of alcohol, and a bad Mussulman is one who pays for his liquor; the simple Mussulman is the one who accepts the proffered bottle, and drinks deeper than the most gin-sodden unbeliever. A good example is never lost. The crew flung themselves upon the other bottles, each sailor snatching his neighbour's, drinking from his own and his fellow's "Black and White." It provoked a violent delirium of rolling which joined that of the breakers, and, not long after, a drowsiness that prophesied well for Ulysses.

Soon, when they were all snoring, Ulysses put his hand to the helm again. Bringing in the sail a little, he luffed to port. When dawn began to break, he saw how close they had been to the rocks. He kept far enough out to avoid them, but not so far as to lose sight of them altogether.

The storm seemed to grow wilder at the first glimmer of daybreak. The Red Sea was white with foam. The Arabs lay deep in drunken slumber. For a whole night and a day, Ulysses was at the helm, which he handled with ever-growing skill.

The morning mist that hung upon the skyline was pierced by a white spot. Ulysses rubbed his eyes, fearing that he was dreaming in the languor of his weariness, or that it was a mirage of the African coast. But the more he looked, the more certain he became that it was a real town. From all the information he had gathered before sailing and during the voyage, it could only be Suakin, so he headed the sambouk thither. Fearing the temper of the Arabs on awakening, when they saw that he had taken charge of the boat, he resolved to cast anchor without their help. But as he drew nearer, he saw that the reefs would be difficult to navigate in spite of the fairer weather. He had almost decided to risk it, when the dangers to overcome, appearing every moment more formidable, made him change his mind. He roused the captain, who was slow in coming to his wits. The sambouk was already among the reefs when the Arab realized what was afoot. With a yell of hatred and fear, he woke his shipmates, crying:

"Brothers, come! We are betrayed! Suakin!"

All the Arabs repeated the words, hurling a flood of insults at the Nazarene. It was then that Ulysses realized that the only port where the sambouk must not call was the port of Suakin, the very town to which he had paid his passage.

[95]

The Arabs became menacing. The captain and the crew made superhuman efforts to disengage the boat from the straits down which she was already drifting, and to head her for the open sea again. Ulysses felt that he was no longer in safety. In the cries of the Arabs the words "guns" and "Tokar" recurred continually. Thanks to the lackadaisy of Haralambos, the Suez freight agent, he was aboard a sambouk whose hold contained, without doubt, a cargo of rifles for the Mahdist dervishes. The captain had found it best not to refuse the handful of pounds which Ulysses had offered for his passage, with the hinder purpose of getting hold of his merchandise as well. So arrival at Suakin, which was occupied by the troops loyal to the Khedive of Egypt, was the greatest misfortune that could overtake them. The Arabs were about to bind Ulysses and throw him overboard, far out to sea. He preferred to throw himself into the water, near the reefs and the harbour. So, abandoning his precious cargo, he took the long plunge.

East of Suez, uncertainty and delay are the masters of destiny.

7

✿✿✿

AFRICA is the place where mankind wears the mask of night. It is the country of deep sleep and wild dreams, where sloth and wakefulness follow each other with irregularity and exaggeration; the continent whose history seems always legend and where all legend is perhaps history. For Africa, which has given the lie to Herodotus for two thousand years, confirms him now. By its giants and its dwarfs, by its gold and its diamonds, by its sun-parched deserts, and by its uncharted rivers, by its wild beasts and its insects, by the brilliance of its plains and the darkness of its forests, by its gods and its wizards, and by its thousand contradictions, Africa is astonishing, baffling, and terrifying. For thousands of years, white humanity has never been more than a slender girdle about this continent. The Phœnicians, the Persians, the Romans, the Greeks, the Dutch, the French, and the English, all those who have ever conquered, have settled on the coasts of Africa. But the further they pushed inland, the more violent became the reaction of the interior, and when they clung to the coast, they felt, but nowhere could they see, a fluid and insurmountable resistance.

For thousands of years, Africa has been the country of partial conquests. Columns of troops have marched victoriously through easily defeated territory; but it has regularly slipped away from them by the agency of an omnipresent strength that is invisible, nameless, devoid of any political entity, and without any known organization. All that has come from the coast has been driven back coastwards again by the black mystery of the interior. Sometimes the phantom has become flesh; the Negroes of Jugurtha made even Rome tremble, and then dispersed and vanished again among their dunes and shifting sands. For the African desert has the strange power of letting anything that comes from the interior filter through to the coast, while it bars the way to all that comes from the coast in search of the hinterland. For the blacks it seems to be porous, like a sieve, but against the whites it is completely proof, to such a point that anyone who wanted to tell a traveller's tale had only to speak of Africa; of this continent no truth, and, therefore, all untruth, was believable.

And if the geography and ethnology of Africa are almost exhausted, does not the mystery of the Negro's soul still remain? Will one ever know what lies behind those low foreheads, those thick lips, and those white teeth? Whether they are pagans or Christians, Ethiopian Monophysites or American Puritans, whether they intone their chants in the way of the fellahin or after the Byzantine, Gregorian, or Lutheran way, will there ever be anything else in the dark depths of their souls but the tom-tom of the cannibals, or the jazz of Louisiana drinking hells? And which will triumph at last, the Christian hymns that we have taught them, or the throbbing jungle dances that we have learned from them? The present hour should surely be fraught with misgivings. The voice of the Negro seems to have become our voice, and his gestures, our gestures. If we have slowly gained possession of his country, is he not acquiring the mastery of our souls? In America, where will the dark flood, which swells that enormous birthrate so heavily, stop? How far will it go when the compensating influx of European immigration will have ceased through inevitable saturation? And even our bodily conquest over them, is it a true-built and abiding one?

All through time, from the Pharaohs to the Khedives, has not the Egyptian followed the Nile upstream, even to its sources, to be suddenly threatened in his turn as far down as the Delta? Have not the English, and now the Italians, grasped at Abyssinia? Who knows what the lot of the conqueror will be? The Boers, the French, the Belgians, the English, and the

Italians may already boast of permanent positions, but let us not forget that Africa is the land of the Senussis, persevering in their secret, tireless energies, and of fearless and terrible Mahdis, believing themselves to be the shadow of God on earth. These illumined mystics, one of whose gestures may suffice to rouse a continent, have existed, and will exist, throughout all history.

Egypt, rich in honours and gold, proud of her legendary past and her glorious present, of her fruitful country, and of her sacred river (hallowed alike in its length and in its deeds), had thrust her empire towards the great lakes, which are the eternal cradles of her wealth. What was there to frighten her? The white men who cast their eyes upon her? Them she distrusted. But how could she fear the wandering blacks, scattered, unarmed, and unorganized, with no resources save for the limitless face of the desert, where one could go astray, or die of hunger or thirst, but never build an empire? For Egypt, her southern frontiers were a halting place, never a boundary. At the whim of her changing fancy, she had continued or broken her march up the Nile. When she retreated, she believed that it was only to solidify herself against invasion from the North or from the East. But the Black Wave would follow her retreat instinctively, and establish the void anew, when the Egyptian tide flowed downstream.

Thus, flux and reflux had been the centuries-old

story of the Sudan, with all that the term contains of fleeting and uncertain.

Now, one day it came about that this impersonal game of African armies changed completely. A man appeared, saying he was the immediate prophet of God, springing directly from Mohammed, and at his voice the black world awoke from its long dream. From the Sudan, from Kordofan, from the lakes, from the hills, from the Red Sea, and from the immense desert, the tribes flocked to the banner of the new prophet. Egypt slowly grew aware of the fervour of the blacks who began to filter through her southernmost marches. The first prophet died before his time, and was succeeded by another, for one of the paradoxes of Islam is the easiness with which the prophetic fire is transmitted; when one man is declared prophet, there is a spark that kindles simultaneously in the breast of his successor.

These two prophets drove back the Egyptian troops, although they were commanded by British generals. An army corps under Hicks was massacred to a man. Another under General Baker was scattered after a defeat that was as crushing as it was ignominious, and Khartoum soon fell in spite of Gordon's heroic defence. Save for Suakin on the Red Sea, the whole Sudan was in the hands of the second Mahdi. For seventeen years he was a constant menace to Egypt. Throughout his long tenure of power, the Mahdi kept his state in order after the best native fashion; he garnered all puissance into his own hands, distributing only the slightest share to his kinsmen, and cutting off the head of anyone who protested.

He was, beyond all gainsaying, a ruler. Sure of his own superiority, but without any personal pride, as it was of divine inspiration, he treated all opposition as blasphemy and sacrilege. On the other hand he was quick to grasp, after the fall of Khartoum, which consecrated the union of his empire, that money is the nerve-string of war and of all true piety. Rising far above many of the scruples that are voiced in the Koran, which, according to the finest minds, are due only to serious errors of rendering, he shielded with the green banner of the Prophet all trade from which he could reap some gain, even though the gain were usurious. The ceaseless warring never hindered his caravans in their search for ivory, the cheapest and the best. His myrmidons and his barques brought the precious elephants' tusks from the Congo, and to gain the greater profit, he had them cut up and burnished in Khartoum. Long strings of camels bore them towards the Red Sea, where the waiting sambouks sailed away eastwards or northwards with their snowy cargo.

His piety, and his communion with God through the Archangel Gabriel, who had already served Mohammed as interpreter in similar cases, did not prevent his examining his accounts, and keeping them in perfect order. Under a system such as his, lying or negligent servants are rare. He thought that his trade

[102]

would gain in breadth and his people in decency if the men, and especially the women, ceased going completely naked.

So, on the banks of the Nile at Khartoum, under the astonished eyes of the crocodiles, he built sheds for wool-washing and weaving and carding. The women took to the new fashion easily and the men without overmuch demur. When there was dearth of raw material, a well-organized round-up supplied it cheaply. He even perfected an armament and powder factory that the Egyptians had established in Khartoum. In religion a mystic, and in finance a protectionist, in politics he was a realist and a centralizer. Having taken Khartoum with a few hundred friendly or allied tribes, he decided to disband them and let them rebuild their hearths as soon as the main work was accomplished. But, well aware of the advantages of the federal system in empire-building, he assembled all their chiefs and elected notables in Khartoum, and kept them at Khartoum as a sort of imperial council. When the empire was founded, he decided that the federal system should be replaced by a more personal and centralized rule, so he kept them as hostages, which facilitated all his dealings with the tribes from which they came. In his piety and centralizing spirit, Mohammed-el-Taishi resembled the good King Louis XI.

He resembled him, too, in the effective simplicity of his methods. But he differed in his sense of honour. Never once did he cut off a hostage's head, the guest being sacred. If some tribe broke its vow of fealty and refused absolute obedience, that passive "*sicut ac cadaver*" which is the right of kings, especially when they are supported by prophecy, he always respected his hostage's life, but annihilated the whole tribe.

Under his sway, the Sudan grew a little less freely populated, certainly, but the sharing of plunder between the survivors was fairer and, above all, more abundant.

All in all, the Mahdi was a real leader. His orders were seldom disobeyed. He had that sovereign quality of men who are born to command; he was continually favoured by fortune. The fall of Khartoum not only supplied him with a capital where he could centralize his administration, which would otherwise have remained disconnected and nomadic; it furnished him with three white persons, and each of them served him after his fashion.

Being gifted with a love of pomp and ceremony, he entered the town flanked by an Austrian nobleman, a cavalry officer who had entered the service of the Egyptian Army, and whom he had made his prisoner. Knowing how to employ each man according to his own genius, he dubbed him his personal squire and principal stableman. As personal squire, the Austrian was in charge of the Mahdi's horses, camels, and asses; as first stableman, or syce, he ran on foot in front of the Mahdi's carriage, horse, camel, or ass, for more than ten years.

Being gifted with the love of charity, which is one with the Mussulman character, he found in Khartoum an old Franciscan sister who succoured the maimed, the sick, and the wounded in every way she could, introducing a strangely gentle touch into the merciless rule of the conqueror.

Being gifted with the sense of administration, diplomacy, and finance, he found Ulysses there, and used him as was fitting.

8

✻✻

ΑT that time Suakin was Egypt's last stronghold on the Red Sea. Tokar, a few miles further south, was already occupied by the dervishes, who scoured the plains so thoroughly that no inhabitant of Suakin dared venture forth. As for the Egyptian garrison, its only activity was that of finding what little food they could, and making it palatable with a pinch of hashish. To keep the courage of the fellahin from flagging—a courage which has been but rarely manifested during their ten thousand years of history—they were each morning told of the immediate, but never realized, arrival of a strong British contingent. It was these encouragements, whose rumour had spread as far as Alexandria, that had brought about the ruin of Ulysses and the sergeant-major.

For more than a year, Ulysses, too, awaited the British troops to whom he had no more beer or whisky to sell but among whom he hoped that more fruitful opportunities would arise than among the Egyptians who had not been paid for two months.

After diving overboard, he reached land at Suakin with neither money nor wares; of all his dreams and savings, nothing remained but the sodden raiment on his back and the unshakable optimism in his soul.

Open his sun-and-salt-seared eyes as he might, nowhere did they fall upon the consoling red jacket of a British trooper. The handful of hungry-looking Egyptian soldiery, the ragged Negroes, the horde of black children paddling in the water, their eyes aswarm with flies, and the cluster of whitewashed hovels chilled his heart. But the murkiest depth of desolation was that he could nowhere find a Greek. The absence of his countrymen amply showed that there was nothing to be done; for they leave a sinking ship like rats. Suakin was a lost town, dead to all profitable trade, and the Mahdi would soon be master of the whole Sudan.

Things being as they were, one had to keep alive somehow. Ulysses found in his cartridge belt, behind the useless cartridges, his last remaining pound. He bought as much string as he could find, and wove himself a net. At first the fish he caught were his only fare. But soon, when he grew skilled in his apostolic calling, he often had a number left over which he sold to some Arab sheikh. Bread began to grace his meals but his pocket remained empty. But his head was always ahum with schemes. Sequestered in this backwater, he lacked all foil for his genius. He dreamed of wonder-

[107]

ful sales and wonderful purchases, but there was neither buyer nor seller to be found, so he had to content himself with the small profits he gained from his fishing. Ulysses was too great for his surroundings. He was desolate and alone.

One day, returning from his day's fishing, he met the mighty Mustafa Aga, the commander of the town, who bade him come to the headquarters immediately. Ulysses could already feel the pains of the bastinado, and the swarming of dungeon rats over his hunger-sunken belly, and the vision of ignominious and early death weighed on his lagging footsteps. At the *caracol*, the police station which did duty as the commander-in-chief's headquarters, his fear deepened when he saw the dirty and hostile appearance of some of the soldiers, who showed no signs of respect towards their superior officer. His misgivings grew when he found himself locked into a dark room without a word of explanation. Now and then he heard the echo of unruly shouts from the guard-room. But Mustafa Aga was not long in coming. He sat down upon the three-legged stool which was the room's entire furniture, and enjoined Ulysses to sit on the floor, politely enough.

After these preliminaries Mustafa Aga plunged into conversation.

"What is thy name?"

"Ulysses."

"Whence comest thou?"

"From Iskanderieh."

"Art thou a Roumi?"

"Without doubt."

"Dost thou know Marko, thy countryman?"

Ulysses had never heard of him, but thought it best to reply:

"By Allah, I know him."

"Where is he now?"

"In these troubled days, no man may know where his own brother is. . . ."

"Thou speakest truly, may the curse of Allah weigh upon the world!"

"Allah is great."

"Thou knowest that Marko trades in the Kordofan, and that the Mahdi (may the dogs eat his carcass!) holds him in high esteem."

Ulysses decided that he had better exaggerate his intimacy with so great a personage.

"Marko is the brother of my mother, and he is mighty among the mighty, how should I not know it?" he affirmed.

"Couldst thou find him again?"

"The undertaking is a difficult one. . . ."

"What needest thou to accomplish it?"

"To know exactly what you want of me, to be informed exactly as to what territory is in the hands of the dervishes (may the dogs eat their carcasses!), and the sum of five hundred pounds to pay the guides, the dervish chieftains, and any bad men I may encounter."

His words pleased Mustafa Aga. They indicated a

particular knowledge of Sudanese conditions, and a general one of the hearts of men.

"By Allah, my son, thy words are wise!" concluded the commander of the Suakin garrison.

Mustafa Aga gave all the explanations that were asked of him. He even unrolled an enormous map that was so spotted and fly-blown that the Sudan seemed more plentifully covered with vast cities than the United States of America. In his own way, the Egyptian strategist explained all the past campaigns of the Mahdi (whose carcass he consigned to the dogs a hundred times), the places he had occupied, the zones he had laid waste, his immediate intentions, and the routes that were least exposed to his fury, from Suakin to the heart of the Kordofan, which he got mixed up with the Belgian Congo. During this staff conference Ulysses decided that, though he knew nothing of the Sudanese hinterland, his knowledge was greater than that of the Egyptian commander; and he regretted that he had asked for only five hundred pounds. He waited to learn what was wanted of him and Marko, of whose name and existence he had had not the slightest notion and whom he had thought fit to make his maternal uncle.

"Your Excellency," he said, "I will certainly be able to find my mother's brother wherever he be, but what am I to say to him?"

"My son, we can hold Suakin no longer. My troops (may the dogs eat their carcasses!) do not want to fight. One day or another, the dervishes of Tokar will attack and slaughter us all. . . . They have been given millions of rifles. . . ."

"By Allah, I know they have," sighed Ulysses.

"It would be more fitting to surrender the town, but whether I surrender it to them, or whether they take it themselves, they will massacre us all, unless an order of the Mahdi——"

"May the dogs eat his carcass!" interrupted Ulysses.

"Marko alone could extract that order from the Caliph. . . . The only garrisons that have not been slaughtered have been saved through the intercession of thy mother's brother, may Allah shield him with His holy protection!"

Ulysses had stood up.

"Your Excellency! Ulysses, the son of Marko's sister, will save Suakin and his Mussulman brethren! Allah is one! By Allah, the Merciful, the Loving-Kind! But the undertaking is harder than I thought. I would have to have at least a thousand pounds. . . ."

"Son of a dog! We haven't got even a thousand piastres!"

"Your Excellency! If I am the son of a dog, I am not the son of the sister of Marko, our saviour. . . . I know that you have not a thousand piastres, I know that the Egyptian Government (may the dogs eat its carcass!) has forgotten you for long months. But I know of a hidden treasure in the town, where many, many pounds are to be found. . . ."

"*Stamfurah el Azim!*" cried Mustafa Aga. "Where? Let me get my hands on it at once!"

"I was great in my own country; I was greater still in Iskanderieh . . . founded by my ancestor. At Suakin destiny has willed that I should be a simple fisherman; I, the son of Marko's sister. But I sell fish to the sheikh Mohammed Baroudi, I cross his threshold when and how I will. He that has eyes and ears, sees and hears many things. Sheikh Mohammed keeps hidden among his women, at the bottom of his haremlik, gold, much gold. Can you take it from him?"

"By Allah! I will take his last piastre! My soldiers shall take his house by storm! If he does not give me his gold with goodwill, he shall have stripes on the soles of his feet till the treasure be found!"

"Your Excellency! More is attained by sweetness than by violence. Go to the sheikh Mohammed, say that you know that he has much gold hidden in the room at the end of his haremlik, under the third tile on the left of the door, beneath the chest where his caftans are kept. He will give it you. . . . Do not take it all. . . . Leave him half. . . . Our Prophet, who has been praised by your own, enjoins all men to give half, but only half, of their goods. One must push no one too far! One must take of everyone only what he can, and should, give to his neighbour!"

"By Allah, my son, thy counsel is good. . . . Of all the sons of Satan thou art the most satanic. How dost

[112]

thou know these things that my police have never discovered in spite of all their searches?"

"Negresses have the devil in their bodies. . . . They love the Roumis. . . . In the haremlik of Sheikh Mohammed there is a Negress whose skin is black as night and sweet as sugar. . . ."

"Thou devil's pimp! By delving in the depths of Sheikh Mohammed's Negresses, thou camest even beneath the tiles on which thou didst lie!"

Mustafa fell to laughing and went on so long that Ulysses feared that he must suffocate. When he was able to articulate again, Mustafa Aga said:

"Go, my son! Go towards happiness! I will have the money tonight, and tomorrow at dawn shalt thou set forth."

But Ulysses left at night.

He could not go to sleep, kept awake by the fear that Mustafa Aga, and, above all, his soldiers, would make ill use of Sheikh Mohammed's treasure. He accompanied the expedition but took no active part in it, so as not to compromise himself in the eyes of his Negress. He stood in the peaceful shadow of the street while the men of war did their work. He followed the hubbub in the harem, the screams of the women, the protestations of Sheikh Mohammed, and finally the return of Mustafa Aga at the canter, followed by four sergeants, one of whom bore a sack that was full to bursting.

[113]

Lest the Egyptian warrior should change his mind, Ulysses resolved to take what he was given, and leave Suakin without losing a minute.

The sack was put on the guard-room table. The news of the trove had drawn all the garrison thither; even the sentries had quit their posts, and sacrificed the sleep which was the prerogative of their office.

The soldiers jostled one another to get as near as possible to the gold. There was a bustle and a shouting, and the warlike spirit of the Egyptian garrison at Suakin had never before displayed so much latent heroism. The authority of Mustafa Aga had been reconsolidated completely by the fiscal qualities that he had displayed in levying and collecting this war tax; but he lost his prestige again by wishing to assume the humble office of cashier. When he prepared to count the money himself, they shouted to him that he was not a saraf—a common money-changer. They reminded him that he was a colonel, that he represented the honour of the Khedive; simultaneously consigning all his gold lace and froggings to the devil, along with the mother who had conceived him. The colonel, attacked on all sides, jostled, reviled, and sweating, almost lost his tarboosh and showed himself bareheaded, the crowning indignity to Mohammedans. Ulysses, mingling with the warlike throng, suddenly shouted that he, like all the Roumis, was a saraf, that he could count money quicker and better than anyone else, and suggested that the task should be entrusted

[114]

to him. The idea had a logical ring. Each Egyptian soldier felt that he had less to fear from the dog of a Christian, that spawn of a base breed, than from his comrades-in-arms. With a many-voiced cry it was decided that the Roumi should count the money. Ulysses was pushed, pulled, almost flung towards the table, where the sack was being propped up by all the fingers that could get near enough to touch it.

Before the anxious eyes of Mustafa Aga, and the covetous eyes of many of his garrison, who stood on tiptoe to catch a better glimpse, their parched lips in a rigour of tortured desire, Ulysses counted quickly and well. He made little piles of twenty pounds, which he arranged in line with the precision of a Prussian parade. He made a fresh pile for each different coinage. Those who were nearest to the table displayed an unctuous tendency to set the heaps of money to rights, calling down upon their heads the protestations and insults of their fellows. At one moment, the table was nearly overturned, so powerfully is the human body tortured by the lust for gold. Ulysses counted aloud in a precise voice. The trove turned out to be of one thousand three hundred pounds, each sovereign bearing the portrait of Queen Victoria and of St. George rearing on horseback over the writhing dragon; of one hundred and twenty-six napoleons; and of eighty Maria Theresa thalers, no doubt from Abyssinia.

The counting was finished. Mustafa Aga called for silence, and in a solemn speech explained to his soldiers the mission that had been entrusted to Ulysses, and all his needs, one by one. They all shouted that he had demanded too much. After a lengthy palaver that lasted almost an hour, in which everyone shouted a reason that nobody heard, in an ape-like confusion of cries and gestures, each one of which was blessed by the name of Allah and the Prophet, sanctifying approval and insult alternately, Ulysses' journey money was reduced to a hundred, to fifty, and even as low as ten pounds, to bounce up again to sixty, down to fifteen, and, finally, up to two hundred pounds.

He put them into his pocket before the whole company. In a supreme access of rhetoric, he gained the thalers too, which he said he would need during the journey, and which, being silver, attracted the Egyptians' cupidity less than the gold. Then began the sharing of the plunder among the officers and men. Things soon began to look ugly. Each one boasted of his rank and service, bellowing murderous ultimatums. Ulysses wanted to slip away, afraid that any agreement would be to his loss, and that disagreement would involve him in a bloodthirsty shambles; so, mastering the hubbub with his foreign and Hellenically ringing voice, he declared that no one would profit by his new fortune, whatever the sharing might be, if the dervishes captured the town; and that, to save it, he, Ulysses, must leave immediately.

This logic seemed reasonable, which is a rare thing in a gathering of men; and, a common thing, nobody wondered how the success of a mission that would take weeks, if not months, could be swayed by a few minutes' delay. With a unanimous cry they admitted that the words of the Roumi were true. Ulysses, for whom way was made immediately, left the guard-room in a murmur of approbation and encouragement, where the predominant words were "Go towards the good!" As he passed, Mustafa Aga even kissed him on both cheeks.

As soon as he was outside the guard-room, the babel began anew. Weighed down with his new fortune, he went and gathered from his boat a flat loaf of Arab bread and a handful of olives, and, lightfoot with hope, vanished into the darkness of the desert and of destiny.

9

❀❀

THE nineteenth century should be called the Century of Africa.

The Protestant missionaries, headed by Livingstone; the Catholic missionaries with Cardinal Lavigerie as their leader; the heroic colony of explorers who dreamed of discovering new territory for their countries; and the humble scattered infiltration of little Greek merchants, dreaming of filling their empty pockets, have slowly lightened the dark continent.

Who shall tell the tale of those lowly traders, facing the swarming perils alone, trafficking in everything with everyone? They made the powerful their defenders, and the humble their helpers, in return for their usefulness and through their gift of the priceless tact of commerce, profiting by handfuls when it was possible and working for nothing when it was opportune.

In every propitious outpost there is certain to be a Greek, led thither by his never-failing instinct, supplying a few Negro families or tribes with whatever European articles they may need, or think they need.

As payment, he takes whatever rubber or ivory they can give him, and, as he is alone and unarmed, no one is afraid of him. The savage is like a wild animal; he rarely attacks. He is dangerous only when he thinks that he is himself in danger. He feels that the small trader who builds himself a hut like his own, casts no eye upon his women, has neither strange uniform nor rifle, riding boots nor crop, is not the forerunner of an army. He knows that, should he kill him, no power will bestir itself; so he leaves him alone. When the Negro feels that he has to do with someone weaker than himself, his heart is softened towards him, and he becomes amenable after his kind. So, in Central Africa, the Greek is liked by the Negro and despised by the powerful white man, whose scorn is aggravated by the desire to show the Negroes that all white men are not the same, thinking thus to affirm their superiority. In the Negro's eyes, he only lowers himself to the level of the others that he despises. The Greek loses nothing by it, and the conquerors, whether they are English, French, or Belgian, much. First, they lose the friendship of the Greek, who, being ever in the Negroes' midst, blackens their name whenever he has the chance; secondly, they lose a precious source of information; and, thirdly, they lose a supple intermediary, well acquainted with all the tortuous mental labyrinths of these primitive peoples.

When the khedives in turn strove to conquer the Nile Valley right up to its sources, many Greeks followed in the rearguard of their armies; and when they retreated, the Greeks remained, like the foam and driftwood that the outgoing tide leaves stranded on the shore.

It was in this fashion that Marko had remained in the Sudan for twenty years, trading everything with everyone. He was often the arbiter in tribal disagreements, chosen by either party. For twenty years he had been turning his long experience of the natives to profit. He knew all the words that they could understand, the only reasonings that they could follow, the only advantages that could appeal to them. The reactions of the black world are not only different from those of the white, but, generally, quite contradictory. What is flattering to the whites is often an insult to the blacks. They feel wounded by a suggested advantage, and some of the simplest reasonings are quite incomprehensible to them, while they can immediately understand others that are extremely complex.

All blacks, and, above all, the Abyssinians, have the distrust of an ever-hunted animal. For some time, Marko had been especially interested in them, for their country was full of merchandise that could be sold at an ever-increasing profit.

To obtain their rubber, Marko had to bring all his patience and cunning into play. Installing himself on the sandy river brink, he fell to gathering black pebbles, which he pretended to choose with care. The Abyssinians were not slow to join him, and for each handful of pebbles they brought him, he would give a mother-of-pearl button in payment. When they brought him too many, he told them that the pebbles had to be perfectly round, and refused most of them. As soon as they were quite convinced that the white man was mad, giving away objects of value for worthless pebbles, he asked them to bring him some skins. They began hunting the same day, and at every sunset brought him skins of all the Abyssinian fauna, believing him born to be cony-caught. As they still seemed to be delighted with the mother-of-pearl buttons that he gave them in payment, the piles of skins in his barn grew bigger, and the time was ripe for launching the essential plan. Marko wanted rubber. He had secretly made one of his porters cut into the bark of a rubber tree. When sufficient gum had accumulated, he had it brought to him, and ostentatiously presented the porter with a fine gilt button. The example was enough. All the trees in the district were brutally mutilated and the gum flowed continually from their wounds, and every day a throng of Abyssinians brought him the precious stuff, returning home wild with joy and gratitude for whatever small chattel Marko had given them in return.

An Abyssinian chief even asked him how many buttons would be given for the blood of his tribesmen, bled in the same way. Marko had great difficulty, and even ran a certain danger, in making it clear to him that the suggested merchandise was valueless. The

[121]

Abyssinian was ready to have half his tribe bled by the other half and fretted over the lost bargain. Marko extricated himself from this unfortunate development and from the excessive zeal that he had provoked by telling the Abyssinian chief that human blood was worthless, and that man alone amongst animals was without market value, as there were no buyers, either for his skin or for the ivory of his teeth. The Ras had to agree, and the rubber went on amassing in Marko's shed, to such purpose that after a few months' sojourn on the banks of the Blue Nile he had made his fortune.

Being a loyal subject, he rendered a tithe of his wealth to the Mahdi, who conceived a great esteem for him. He decided that the Nazarenes, although they were sons of dogs, were more useful subjects than the most orthodox dervishes. He forbade all his followers to touch a hair of Marko's head; so Marko became a sort of great vassal, the wealth behind the throne; the Fugger of this equatorial emperor.

As the Egyptian soldiers resisted but feebly bullet and spear-blade, but gave way even more readily before silver thalers stamped with the effigy of Maria Theresa, Marko advised the Mahdi to use this metal more than the others. Thanks to him, the surrenders of all the conquered towns and garrisons were much less bloody than they would have been. His intercession saved many Egyptian lives, along with those of a certain number of dervishes whom the Egyptian warriors always killed by mistake, without any murderous intent, and with the sole wish to justify, by a few shots, their immediate retreat, which was always prompt from long days of waiting and expectancy. This specific and pecuniary strategy had the greatest success, and delighted the Mahdi. If the Mahdi was the shadow of Allah on Sudanese earth, Marko became his vicar *in partibus infidelium*. His diocese lay wherever there was ivory, skins, or rubber, or an Egyptian garrison that wished to surrender without being massacred. It was thus that his great renown had reached Suakin, and attracted the attention of the commander of the garrison there. At that time Marko was busy collecting his skins and rubber to embark them at El Teb on the Red Sea coast. He had pitched camp on the Atbara and enrolled several caravans of coolies. Being on excellent terms with a certain Osman Digna, the Mahdi's ally and representative in those parts, he never lacked for men to transport his merchandise. His camp was like a giant ant-hill. The Negroes ran to and from the river and the sheds; the bundle-mounds were growing apace; everything was numbered and trussed with rope; the tasks were fairly allotted; and Marko presided over the many-faceted labour from dawn till sundown.

One evening in his hut, when he had laid himself down on a panther skin to read by candlelight a three-month-old Greek newspaper from Alexandria, his servant entered and announced the arrival of a white man. Marko rubbed his eyes as if he were dreaming. (The last white man he had seen, more than a year before, had been the corpse of Hicks Pasha, over whom, as a makeshift for Christian burial, he had made the sign of the cross and pronounced, before a mob of dervishes drunk with killing, the only words of the Orthodox funeral ceremony that he knew: "Receive the last kiss; may thy memory rest eternal."

Leaping from his couch, he saw a living white man standing before his hut, backed by a crowd of bewildered Negroes. To himself he cried:

"Come, Christ and the Holy Virgin!"

He felt at once that the newcomer was a fellow-countryman.

"You are welcome," he said, stretching out his two hands towards him.

"You are well found," answered Ulysses, taking the two hands and raising them to his lips.

"Come, my son, that I may kiss you," said Marko.

And the two Greeks, lost in the black ocean, kissed each other long and many times. Putting his arms about Ulysses' waist, Marko pushed him towards his hut.

"Where do you come from?" he asked.

"From Suakin. . . ."

"How long did you take to find me?"

"About two months," answered Ulysses.

"You must be hungry and you must be tired."

Marko called the Negro who tended him as body-servant, and bade him set all that the hut could provide before Ulysses: milk, a roasting of antelope, and, supreme Hellenic joy, bubbling coffee in a minute cup.

While Ulysses ate in silence, Marko watched him with the admiration of one who could fitly judge of his sort of adventure. From time to time, he tapped him on the shoulder, crying:

"What shall I say to you? You are truly the son of a mother!" which, in modern Greek, expresses enthusiasm for a deed well done.

When Ulysses' hunger was appeased, Marko said:

"Now tell me how it is that you came from that direction."

Ulysses told him of his sojourn at Suakin and of the mission on which he came. Marko interrupted him many times, exclaiming:

"By the Truth! You are the devil's very own sock!"

When he heard that Ulysses carried two hundred pounds and some thalers with him, he made haste to say, on the subject of the Egyptian garrison at Suakin:

"Let those dogs eat their own dung!" adding immediately:

"You will stay with me. I need a man of your kidney. I can't do everything alone. . . . Now tell me how you found me and how you escaped the dervishes, may the devil take their father!"

Ulysses told of his wanderings, as all simple men and heroes tell of their deeds, without phrases. His tale had no object in the telling. He told of all the circumstances as they came, ungarnished and without comment. The men who do great things do them unaware of their greatness. Should they know, it would crush them and they would waver and fail. It is only the shadow of things before the sun of the imagination that fills the breast with fear. Like all realists, Ulysses lacked imagination, save for the shaping of his future deeds. For him all deeds, and the memory that lingered after them, were adorned by no emotional halo.

Seated at Marko's table, Ulysses forgot his hunger and thirst in the desert. The fact of his present security superseded and suppressed the fact of his past dangers. Now that Marko was found, nothing remained of all the hardships he had suffered in the finding. He felt the unformulated terror of night time and the torrid heat of day no longer; nor the always embarrassing and sometimes threatening questions of the dervishes. His plan accomplished, all former impressions were lost in the principal reality, which was alone of import.

To Marko's questions as to how he had had the courage to set out on such an enterprise, Ulysses answered with simple reasoning:

"As you alone could save the Egyptian garrison, I was sure that the dervishes would know your name and whereabouts. I answered every question with: 'Where is Marko?' That question saved my life a hundred times, and they always set me on my right course. The dervishes offered me their hospitality as soon as I men-

[126]

tioned you, and when they saw that the way was difficult to follow, they gave me a guide to the next village.
My journey there was like that of a parcel sent from
post office to post office."

Marko, proud of his countryman, listened with the
approving kindness of an old wayfarer, astonished by
nothing, but quick to appreciate the successes of his
juniors.

"And where do you keep your money?" he asked.

"In this belt," answered Ulysses; "take it; it will be
safer in your keeping."

"No, keep it, my child. Here in the desert one can
never know what the morrow may bring forth. And
you and I might be killed. If one escapes, he had better
have some money on him; for they do not bury corpses
here; they strip them."

"Are you still afraid of the dervishes, in spite of
your renown amongst them?"

"Listen, Ulysses my child; one can never know what
may happen with the Mussulmans. . . . A word, a
drop of liquor, a pinch of hashish, a verse of the Koran,
or a mullah's speech may unlock the gates of their
fury. They turn from lambs to lions before you know
where you are. After their Mahdi, I am the most loved
and respected amongst them; but, nevertheless, I am
only a Nazarene, whose death would whisk the killer
straight to Paradise. God preserve mankind from the
fury of the Moslems! With them, as in one's dealings
with women, one's eye must be as keen as the eagle's,

[127]

one's foot swift as a hare's, and one's sleep as light as a watchdog's."

"And what are we going to do now?" asked Ulysses.

"Not so fast. Everything in its season and codfish in August. Night is for sleep, day is for work. We will talk tomorrow. . . . I have a plan for you. . . ."

"Good! But I must do something; up to now I have gone from failure to failure. The English have deceived me, and the Arabs too."

Ulysses told the story of his adventures, from his leaving Alexandria to his arrival at Suakin. Nothing in the telling seemed to astonish Marko. He limited his comments to the underlining of the important passages by the word "*κερατάδες*," adorning with richness and variety of epithet the horns of all the enemies of Ulysses, from the sponge-fishers to the captain of the sambouk, dealing with Barba Dimitri, Kyria Lenio, the sergeant-major, and Haralambos on the way. On learning of the favour with which he was looked upon by Negresses, he made him swear by "the Saint" not to touch a single woman in the Mahdi's kingdom. He ended with the words:

"Here in the desert we are at war. No one knows who will be his enemy tomorrow. The enemy of yesterday is seldom the enemy of today. . . . In these conditions it is death to lay one's hand to a woman's girdle. It brings bad luck. And now let us sleep!"

Ulysses was asleep already. Marko stayed up a little while, turning the pages of a greasy ledger. It contained his accounts, and his journal from day to day. All his purchases, receipts, and deliveries were written out in it. There were all his debtors and creditors. There were his true accounts for his own use, his false ones for the use of others. There were the orders he had given and received, the bargains he had struck. There was all the information he required, and which, for the last few days, had become more and more disturbing. There was the little picture of the Blessed Virgin that he kissed before going to bed every night, and which he kissed that night with unaccustomed fervour. Marko watched for a long time over the sleeping Ulysses. The fresh and unwonted sweetness of having a fellow-countryman by his side was so delightful that he wanted to savour it as long as possible. He struggled against the sleep that would rob him of it, and in the heavy silence of the African night, broken with hallucinating regularity by the jackal's laughter, the older man recalled the dreams of his youth, while the younger one dreamed of the older's triumphs.

For more than a month Marko had been brooding over a mighty secret. A messenger had handed him a seal, the guarantee of the news he brought: the English were coming to the relief of Khartoum, hoping to make it the kernel of their imminent reconquest of the Sudan. They were already at Korti, ready to cross the desert that lay in the bend of the Nile. Colonel Stewart counted on Marko for the victualling of his troops, in the heart of the Mahdi's country. . . . The arrival of the English would mean deliverance or death. For years he had awaited the British offensive, for, of the Egyptians left to themselves, he expected nothing. The massacre of Hicks and the defeat of Baker had augured well for him. He knew that England always avenged the death of her children and all insults flung at her honour. But England could bide her time, and Marko was in a hurry. A hundred times he had heard that British columns had disembarked at Suakin or El Teb, but they had never come. A hundred times the anonymous rumour of the desert had whispered in his ear that a British flotilla was sailing up the Nile. But only the Mahdi's barques plied whither they would, unheeded. He had had to gain the Mahdi's confidence. He had done everything for him, continuing to work for England the while. He was in continual contact with Gordon, who was sequestered and besieged in Khartoum. A barbaric, anarchistic, cruel, and arbitrary country, under the sway of fanaticism and koranic madness, where crime sanctifies the criminal and where blood is the freshest and most abundant dew of heaven, is full of possibilities if one can but leave it at will; and Marko could not leave it until it was conquered by the British. He knew that he was too useful and too dangerous to escape surveillance. The sheikhs who honoured him with their protection, the slaves who kissed his hands, both were alike the masters of his destiny. While he served, he was free, but as soon as he attempted flight, he knew that he would be a prisoner. Now Gordon had asked him for three hundred head of cattle. Where could he find them? How could he collect them and set them on their way Khartoumwards? And he alone could do it. Gordon distrusted Cairo and the Egyptian General Staff. He had been given no white troops, and Cairo teemed with the Caliph's spies. In the fastnesses of the black country, across the empty zones of the Red Sea at the bend of the Nile, the cattle could reach Gordon. It was the safest way. And it was a task for Ulysses; for Marko was forced to remain where he was. He was too well known and loved that death should not strike him at his first suspicious action.

During the eight days that Ulysses had been with him, he had been turning these things over in his mind. Plenty of cattle was shipped through the Red Sea, coming from Australia or Abyssinia. Ulysses could reach an Ethiopian port where the cattle-ships put in, and perhaps strike a good bargain.

Ulysses was "the devil's stocking." But the secret would have to be kept unbroken. No one would know whither he went. Africa was full of the Mahdi's agents, and Abyssinia pullulated with them.

After making Ulysses swear secrecy by the life of his mother and by the Blessed Virgin, after making him kiss the cross of his two forefingers, Marko revealed his plan. Ulysses replied:

"May I be dishonoured, may I be damned, if I do not deliver the cattle to Gordon!"

"Well said, by the Saint! You speak as if you were my own son, spawn of the devil! But let us go slowly. . . . Listen well to all that I tell you. . . . This is no joke, like the others in which you have succeeded so well until today. It is a very great undertaking, one that will make you rich, but it is full of pitfalls and brambles. . . . The dervishes are all hornwearers, hornwearers are the Abyssinians too. Trust nobody, not even yourself. You might talk in your sleep, and then all our plans will go to the devil, and the devil will have the hide off your back."

These words filled Ulysses with an anguish of prudence, but strengthened his determination. The more dangerous the enterprise, the more plenteous the reward.

"You have got two hundred pounds and I shall give you eight hundred more. With that you can buy enough to resell four thousand pounds' worth of cattle to Gordon."

"How much of it do I keep?"

"Keep it all. If God send that we meet again later on, we will talk about sharing then. I am not after profit in this enterprise; it will suffice to have been of service to the English and you, and to have escaped the dervishes (may the devil take their father!) and to have violated the Mahdi's faith (may he be cursed for a century of centuries!)."

"Amen," concluded Ulysses piously. "I am your man! But where shall I find the cattle?"

"That's your business! Open your eyes and do your best."

"I have understood," said Ulysses.

"The only advice I can give you is to make for an Abyssinian port: Massawa, perhaps. Once there, get hold of the first cargo of cattle or sheep you find. Then you charter the ship and disembark between El Teb and Suakin. 'For better or for worse,' I shall give you letters to the Mahdist and Abyssinian chieftains. If you get into difficulties, say that you are driving the cattle to the Mahdi himself, and that whoever interferes with you shall answer with his head."

"I have understood," replied Ulysses. "When shall I set out?"

"Tomorrow, before daybreak. To avoid all indiscretions, I shall give you no guide. You go towards the sunrise; at dawn the sun must be straight in front of you and at dusk it must be straight behind you."

At dawn Ulysses resumed his lonely way, accompanied by Marko's benedictions.

"Go towards the good, my child! . . . May God be with you!"

As he watched the figure of Ulysses dwindling in the distance, Marko, that veteran of Sudanese adventure, murmured to himself:

"That child is the delight of God. . . . He has got the devil in him. . . ."

In the modern Greek mind, God and the devil collaborate intimately in the government of mankind.

[133]

10

❀❀❀❀❀❀❀❀❀❀❀❀❀❀❀❀❀❀❀❀❀❀❀❀❀❀❀❀❀❀❀❀❀❀❀❀❀❀

Tokar, which was in the hands of Osman Digna,
the Mahdi's lieutenant, was the headquarters of the
Sacred Horde on the Red Sea. Through Tokar, and
the port of El Teb, they received supplies of all kinds
of arms, even some antique cannons which they occa-
sionally used, with bloodier slaughter among their own
gunners than in the enemy's ranks. Ulysses, with the
strategic instinct of those who take destiny into their
own hands, reached it by the shortest road. With the
plan of provisioning the English, he saw that the dervish provision centre was the best fitted to fulfil that
plan. Armed with Marko's recommendations, he was
received by Osman Digna like a son. He brought fresh
news. It was all favourable save for the advance of a
strong British column up the Nile and through the
desert, coming to Gordon's rescue, which he took care
not to mention. He also omitted all reference to the
defeat of the dervishes at Abu Klea. Osman Digna,
therefore, kissing him Mussulman-fashion on both

[134]

shoulders, could justly cry: "Allah is great! and blessed is he that announces His victories!"

But, being rather a collector than an announcer of news, Ulysses passed several weeks of intense observation at Tokar. He liked talking with the captains of the sambouks that brought arms to the Mahdi from Arabia and Abyssinia. He even took part in a Mahdist council of war, where Osman Digna and his pirates resolved to seize the British steamship that one of the sambouk captains had passed at Djibouti, taking on a cargo of oxen, and without doubt destined to pass through the Suez Canal. This cargo augured good cheer and the Mahdi's especial favour. It was doubtless destined to provision the Egyptians at Suakin.

After long discussion, in which he discovered that Mohammedans count more upon the help of the Prophet than upon clearly conceived and well-carried-out ideas, Ulysses suggested a plan which won universal approval. His plan was simple. A sambouk would pass by when the British craft was well out to sea. Ulysses would be on board. The presence of a Roumi would inspire the confidence of the English captain. They would lie in wait on the steamer's path, which the pirates knew well, as their calling mainly consisted in avoiding it. When the steamer came in sight, the sambouk would steer towards it. Ulysses would fall into the water. The English, charitable folk, would stop to rescue him, and the sambouk's crew would profit by the British altruism to swarm up the ladder and seize the ship. Osman Digna was so delighted with this project that he called Ulysses his son, a sign of particular affection, and "son of a dog," a sign of supreme admiration.

Ulysses, like all great diplomats, had spoken nothing but the truth; but not the whole truth. The captain of the sambouk who was appointed to carry out the plan did not fail to point out to Ulysses the great danger that he ran. He described the long schools of sharks that infest those waters, and always follow the steamers. He even laughingly avowed that neither he nor any of his crew would dive in to help him if the steamer did not stop in time. But after his dive before Suakin, Ulysses had lost his faith in the appetite of sharks.

They set sail next morning, and did not have long to wait, for, as the third day dawned, a plume of smoke appeared on the southern horizon. The sambouk sailed straight towards it, while the Arabs cleaned and loaded their rifles. Soon the captain recognized the vessel he had seen at Djibouti, and cursed the captain and all the sailors aboard her, crying: "May their houses fall to the ground!" Ulysses arranged that as soon as he was in the water the sambouk should hoist the distress signal, and draw far enough away from him to excite the pity of the steamer, and, straying hither and thither, should sail into the wind only when the steamer's lifeboat had already taken him on board.

The steamer was only two or three cables off. Ulysses buckled his money-belt a hole tighter and dived.

He sank long and deep in a giddiness of rushing water. When he came to the surface, he kept himself afloat with one arm and, signalling desperately with the other, watched the steamer come closer, and the sambouk grow smaller and smaller in the distance. The steamer drew up to him, stopped, and lowered a boat. Thinking that they had rescued an Arab, the English, ever slow to catch the meaning of the unforeseen, failed to understand the presence of a Greek, fallen from a Mohammedan sambouk, among the waves of the Red Sea. Realizing that they had saved a Christian of an inferior race (not being English), instead of a Moslem or some other dark-skinned pagan, their oaths gave ample proof of their disillusion. The English, imperialists by instinct, can respect only the races they have conquered or that they hope to conquer; this present or future submission is the only quality that they can distinguish in foreigners.

When he was taken before the captain, Ulysses understood from his reception that he had profited by a mistake. But he was too wet to be susceptible. He was too jubilant, also, to see the sambouk sailing further and further south till she was only a speck on the horizon. Despite his condition, he experienced a moment of pride when he saw that the peg, with which he had jammed the rudder at the last moment, still held firm, and prevented the sambouk from turning about. All that now remained was to buy up the cargo and disembark it. He started by asking the captain to take him to his cabin, as he wanted to tell him something that no one must hear. When he saw his girdleful of gold, the captain offered Ulysses a whisky and soda. When he heard his proposal, he offered him a second. When the bargain had been struck, he poured out a third, and offered him an immense cheroot.

As the matter in hand was the revictualling of his countrymen, the Englishman was proud to link a patriotic duty with an unhoped-for price for his cargo. But his patriotism appeared only after they had come to terms. Before, he had briefly stated that he could consider only the interests of his company, while Ulysses had insisted on the patriotic nature of the deal. They finally agreed on a disembarkation point; far enough from Suakin to avoid all fear of confiscation from that quarter, and far enough too from El Teb, lest Ulysses, instead of one day seeing the heads of his cattle struck with a pole-axe, should feel his own fall to the ground, cleanly smitten off by the scimitar of Osman Digna.

So Ulysses became a cowherd. After landing, he was once more engulfed by the desert. Accompanied by a guide whom he had found on the coast, he recruited volunteers on the way, from that vague humanity that wanders in the wake of caravans, ready to render any service to the living and to strip and plunder the dead. He pressed forward in the mystery of the short summer nights, sleeping for a few hours in the furnace of the long and merciless days. He had an eye for every-

thing. His beasts cropped the sparse dry grass blades.
He watered them at those little yellow desert pools
that parody, rather than recall, the blessing of water.
At each halting place, some were found missing, fallen
by the way, exhausted by heat, hunger, and thirst.
Following the desert way, Ulysses and his Negroes
drank of their blood while it was still warm, and left
them to be devoured by the host of vultures that
watch from on high for the fall of desert wayfarers.
Hour followed hour, each one the same as its herald;
sad hours of an infinite distress, unsweetened and endless. Day followed day mortally alike, with no possible
relief on the morrow. For weeks, he had to do that
which for weeks he had already done. In the desert,
an ever-deepening lassitude saps little by little the very
foundations of hope, and finally bestrews the road
with whole caravans, when the will to live has been
overcome by the monotony of immutable pain. For
the last time, empty of hope, the eye contemplates the
endless track towards the ever-fleeting horizon; the feet
refuse the next step; the body is overwhelmed by an
insupportable heaviness; for some while still the soul,
the mainspring, drives the automaton forward, stripped
of all hope; then the man or beast collapses. The
stronger pass on without a glance, without a memory,
without pity for the sluggard, who, soon alone on the
burning sand, vanishes into annihilation. Then, all
that can live in the desert, the hyena, the jackal, and
the vulture, come to feast upon his body. He is torn

[139]

to shreds with claws and teeth and beaks, whose skirmishing breaks the yellow silence with its savage tumult, till they disperse to other hunting grounds, leaving, in the haste of their departure, nothing behind them but a few forgotten bones.

Ulysses drove his dwindling herd onward. At each halt he tallied the living and deducted the number of the dead. Already more than half of them had died, and he herded the meagre survivors westward, ever westward, where some day he hoped to see the soft Nile mist, amid the immense surrounding drought. Once he reached the English, Ulysses would have no fear for his losses. The survivors would pay for their dead fellows, and to spare, for supplies, in the desert, are paid according to the inevitable losses and the exceptional dangers that always accompany them. Ulysses ruminated over his reward, chewing and rechewing it. He quenched his thirst with it, he lived on it. If, as poets tell, sailors' hearts are sheathed in threefold brass, those of all great merchants of the African desert are sheathed in the gold of which they dream.

Munching a few dried dates, drinking, in the hollow of his burning hands, a few drops of greenish water drawn from the standing pools, Ulysses watched over everything. He drove his cattle with a long reed, bringing back the beasts that strayed, digging at the sinking Negroes who fell asleep from weariness. His men, recruited haphazard on the road, would disperse in the same way, as mysteriously as they had come. Every day Ulysses became aware of fresh disappearances and arrivals.

The desert Arab lacks endurance. He sets out with a good heart, but abandons everything at the first difficulty. He knows too well what snares and threats lurk in the mirage-haunted sand-dunes. As soon as he can take shelter or reach a near-by oasis, he leaves all that he has undertaken in search of a relative security.

One morning, a Negro climbed a threadbare palm tree, and scanned the horizon for a long time; then, like the muezzin who sings the glory of God from the height of a minaret, he repeated twenty times the magic syllable of the Sudanese desert: "*Bahr! Bahr!*" —"The River! The River!" The Arabs took up the strain and chanted the dream-word in unison; for in Islam everything is sung: work, and suffering, and joy.

Ulysses contented himself with the words: "Glory be to God! We are there!" and with an eye that was skilled by two months of daily reckoning, he counted his herd for the last time. He still had about two hundred beasts. He decided there and then to ask for thirty pounds a head, and to receive at least twenty.

Towards nightfall he saw a fire in the distance which could only be that of a small encampment; a golden glimmer in the melancholy dark. Ulysses walked towards it. Soon a Negro cried: "Dervishes!"

"Inglis! The English!" replied Ulysses, to whom what he wished always seemed truest.

It was in vain that the Negro tried to explain that

the English were not fools enough to light fires, to attract the Mahdi's ambushes.

For Ulysses believed in his star, which had taken the form of a British campfire.

He reached it late at night, and was received with all the honours due to his two hundred lean Abyssinian oxen, which the desert had reduced to skeletons, but which nevertheless appeared delicious to the famished outpost of Stewart's army.

After leaving the fruitful banks of the Nile at Korti, two months before, the English had kept alive on only tinned food and biscuits. The reception of Ulysses, and above all of his oxen, was triumphal. Crossing their arms, and joining hands in a ring, they danced round and round Ulysses, singing:

"For he's a jolly good fellow!"

For the first time in his life, Ulysses felt a hero. For the first time, that night, he felt the promptings of a possible climb to the loftiest social peaks. He, a wretched drover, a humble go-between in the most sordid enterprises, felt himself somebody at last.

At the first dawn the bargain was struck. The general staff of the expeditionary force paid him out a thousand pounds in gold and gave him a cheque for four thousand pounds, on an Alexandrian bank, payable on condition that he should deliver a hundred head of cattle in Khartoum itself, where Gordon was still holding out in desperate need of immediate provisions.

Ulysses accepted this new mission and its certain profits with delight, and set out up the Nile after two short days of rest. He was offered a military escort which he deemed wiser to refuse. Alone, he had less to fear from the dervishes. Between Greek and Arab, things would be easily handled, while, in a possible encounter, the English would introduce a belligerent note that Ulysses preferred to avoid. Besides, should he fall in with one of the Mahdi's patrols, he would make haste to deliver up his cattle, declaring it a homage offered by his master Marko to the greatest of living prophets. The presence of British redcoats would compromise the verisimilitude of such an elegant solution.

As ill chance would have it, Ulysses reached Khartoum without meeting any of the Mahdi's men. He crossed the neutral zone between the British outposts on the Nile and the besieged town, following the river's banks under cover of the sand cliffs.

As soon as he entered Khartoum, he realized that he was in a lost town. From the first words he exchanged with an Egyptian sergeant, he learned that General Gordon had lost his faith in all save God and that everyone else had lost his faith in Gordon. In the general's faith and the scepticism of the troops he saw that the Evil Hour was not far off. As soon as he had delivered his cattle and settled his accounts, he meant to flee northward, but, being without cattle to offer the Mahdi as a gift from Marko, he was forced to be prudent. Haunting the countless cafés, where the Egyptian soldiery sought comfort and distraction from the sorrows of the siege, he made friends with Gordon's orderlies and with a few Egyptian non-commissioned officers. Alas! during the few days that he had been in Khartoum, the imminent arrival of the British rescue column had driven the Mahdists to beleaguer the town still closer, and at the direct approach to the town the Nile was seen to be already aswarm with their vessels.

Flight was impossible. Besides, the final assault cut short all Ulysses' other strategical considerations.

One night, he was awakened by the sound of rifle fire. He ran to the battlements. For, in this warlike time, he too had become a warrior. But, knowing that a good retreat is worth a hundred victories, he meant to take the first opportunity of climbing out of the trap into which he had fallen. This enforced his presence in the front rank.

There, below the bastions, he saw an army of relentless shades that encircled the town, drawing every moment closer; and other hunger-stricken ghosts, who, having lost both the strength and the will to fight, made a futile and half-hearted gesture of defence. Towards daybreak, the plain, the river bank, and even the river itself, were seething with a mighty host of savages, and the sky was filled with their howling, a long-drawn and terrifying cry for blood. Lance-heads flashed in the first glimmers of dawn, and forests of coloured banners topped with horse-tails flapped wildly in the morning breeze.

The name of Allah, howled in every key, no longer signified prayer, but madness. Through being screamed at the top of thousands of voices, it was like an immense, sinister hiccup. Before the squall of that mighty name, made more fearsome still by the howling and screaming, the Egyptians fell back, as a sea-bird yields to terror before it feels the first breath of the storm. The war-cry of the Mahdists had prevailed even before the assault began, but when the attack was launched, the whole world seemed shaken with terror. The dark flood flung itself like a giant wave from the sea's bottom, bearing in its foam-topped breakers all the monsters of the deep. The rifle fire, and the few cannon shots that were released, mowed down a little of the vanguard without staying its fury; flung forward in their maniac charge, even the dead fell into the town on top of the defenders. And the garrison yielded more to the weight of the invaders than to the force of their arms. The ramparts, soon stripped bare of the soldiers who had manned them, were already in the Mahdi's hands. His bare-headed warriors, their eyes starting from their sockets, their lips twisted and howling, their hands clenched on the hilts of their bloody scimitars, or on the shafts of their lances, whence strips of flesh were hanging, swarmed over the town in search of chests to rifle, heads to sever, and bellies to disembowel, in a frenzy of looting and slaughter.

On the highest step before his palace door, the pale Englishman, surrounded by a group of officers of all races, some fellow-countrymen, some foreign mercenaries, and a few Negroes who had remained faithful to his mystic personality, awaited death quietly, his Bible in his hand and his eyes alight with the ecstasy of martyrdom.

This group, erect and grim, was like a fiery bastion. All, save for the stainless general, emptied their firearms so fiercely into the overwhelming throng that there was a moment of hesitation, almost of defeat. But all at once the Mahdi himself, immense and terrible on his white charger, raised his banner towards heaven and cried:

"My brothers! God alone is great!"

And the black tide surged over the palace. Gordon and his guard were crushed, trampled, slaughtered to a man. The invaders gathered about the prophet, while the corpses underfoot still throbbed in their brief agony, their death-rattle inaudible in the cries of victory. Soon a still serene head appeared on the point of a lance; the head of the hero stripped of fear and hope, who, till the end, had done his duty to his country and to his God.

11

✦✦

ULYSSES' first audience with the Mahdi was not
a pleasant one. When, watching the storm sweep over
the battlements, he saw that flight was impossible, he
went into hiding under a mound of Mahdist corpses.
He thought that their sanctified bodies would shield
him better than those of the Egyptians; and he arranged them in such a fashion that they quite covered
but did not suffocate him. The blood that flowed from
their fresh wounds seemed a miraculous dew that,
once dried, might perhaps serve him as an amulet
against a destiny that was charged with immediate
perils. . . . For two days, half dead with anguish and
horror, he lived under his reeking shelter. When, after
their two long days of orgiac bloodshed, the conquerors fell to burying their dead, and he heard the wailing of Moslem dirges, and, peeping wild-eyed between
the bodies, whose decay was gradually changing the
planned symmetry of his dwelling, he saw the buriers
at work, Ulysses realized that the supreme moment

was upon him. When they lifted one of the corpses that protected him, he stiffened in feigned death, in a last hope that the Mussulmans would fling his infidel carcass into the water, and that, once more, he could save his life by swimming.

A horrible cry robbed him of all hope. The words, "The Nazarene is alive!" rang in his ears like a death sentence. Like Christ, he said: "The hour is at hand." A fierce lance-thrust, which happily glanced off one of his lean ribs, recalled the last word that ends the service of the Passion on Good Friday; he said to himself:

"Τετέλεσται"—"It is finished!" and covertly made the sign of the cross.

Rough hands dragged him to his feet. He let himself sag like a corpse. In vain, however, for they jerked him up again. They wanted him alive to kill. But, the Mahdi having reserved the judgment of the white men for himself, they drove him before the Leader with fist, kick, and lance-point, threatening him with tortures of which the sweetest was impaling.

He felt himself suddenly flung to the ground, a miserable shred of humanity. He divined, rather than saw, that he was in the Presence. He was wrenched to his feet. Not daring to open his eyes, he glimpsed, in one instantaneous flutter of his eyelids, the Prophet, the Leader, and the Conqueror, seated, surrounded by a court of eunuchs who laughed with a laugh that boded evil. Ulysses clasped his head with both hands, feeling

[148]

that it was about to be smitten from its trunk. Behind him he felt a hundred scimitars ready to sever his neck at a sign from the master; the icy touch of a razor-sharp blade contracted the whole of his skin with terror.

Almost unconscious, he flung to Allah and to His shadow on earth the one word that he thought might help him:

"Marko!"

"May the devil take Marko's father!" was the bellowed answer from several of the Master's lieutenants. Only the Master held his peace. Strong in this silence, Ulysses stood up. Twenty fists struck him to earth again, then set him on his knees in the classical position of immediate decapitation.

But soon he heard a deep voice, the voice of the great leaders, who, being lords of mankind, have no need to shout.

"Nazarene, why art thou here, thou son of a dog? Thou art too poor to be a merchant like all thy countrymen (may their houses fall to the ground!) and too weak to be a warrior."

Trusting in dialectic, Ulysses felt that safety lay in dialogue, even when it was engaged in under such adverse circumstances. Instinctively, he decided to lead the conversation as far as possible. He felt that wise words alone could save his tottering head. Is not the spoken word the token of life, are not death and silence always concomitant? He said:

"Most powerful Lord! May Allah protect thy sword,

thy seed, and thy faith! Prophet among prophets! God alone is great. In the name of Allah the Merciful, the Loving-Kind, hear the last words that my tongue shall utter, and may it rot in my mouth if I speak one word that is not the truth of God!"

"Of which God?" interrupted the Mahdi. "Of the God of the Nazarenes (may the devil take their father and their mother!)?"

"There is no god but God," cried Ulysses without going so far as to say, "and Mohammed is His Prophet." Such a declaration of apostasy seemed too compromising to the salvation of his soul, if, in spite of everything, it should have to leave his body.

> *"I speak the truth by Allah*
> *He knoweth what is*
> *In the Heavens and in the Earth;*
> *He knoweth all that ye conceal*
> *And all that ye reveal;*
> *For Allah is the Knower*
> *Of the hearts of men!"*

This quotation from the Koran made a good impression; better still, when Ulysses added:

"Besides, art thou not the last prophet of Allah? That which He knows, canst thou not know it also? Who would be mad enough to lie to thee? Why question me even, thou who knowest the contents of my breast?"

This statement of his clairvoyant prophetism visibly

[150]

pleased the man of God. He turned to his following, which, though it regretted that Ulysses' head had some chance of remaining on his shoulders, could not but recognize the inspired knowledge that had just gratified their leader.

Ulysses had the satisfaction of hearing several scimitars rattling back into their scabbards. Only the headsman, whose thirst for blood apparently filled him with scepticism, inflicted an insolent prick on his right buttock, and filled his ear with a threat of unmentionable tortures. The headsman counted without the prophet, who, having received the homage of Ulysses and his court, said in a solemn voice:

"I know what lies in thy heart, by Allah! but I command thee to reveal it to the others, to my faithful companions, who, through their courage and their victories, deserve to hear from thy mouth that which I already know."

As he thus became the very voice of the prophet speaking through his prisoner's mouth, Ulysses knew that he could lie with impunity.

He explained at length his relationship with Marko, his mission, the dangers he had run in accomplishing it, his trail across the desert; how he had been taken prisoner by the English, forced to bring to Gordon the oxen that were destined for the prophet, and how he had tried to find him after all. To support this last affirmation, he pointed to the way that he had been discovered near the ramparts, where the assault had taken him unawares. Had it not been to escape to the besiegers, would he, a civilian, have been found there? In peroration, a drop of Demosthenean blood subsists in the veins of every Greek; so, raising his two hands towards heaven, he cried:

"O Prophet! O Victorious One! O Wielder of the Sword of Allah! May my head fall! May it roll in the mud and in the dogs' droppings! May a horse mangle it! May my tongue parch in the flames of Gehenna! May each one of these lances pierce my bosom! Behold! I drag myself to thy august feet. I would die happy shouldst thou but incline thy greatness towards my lowness, and permit me to kiss the lobe of thy ear, full of the revelations of Allah!"

Saying this, he dragged himself up to the Mahdi, who leant towards him, and, pressing his lips against the lobe of the prophet's ear, Ulysses murmured:

"I have an English paper that is worth five thousand pounds sterling if I live—but, if I die, nothing!"

Saying which he fell like a dead man into the dust at the conqueror's feet.

The Mahdi rose.

"By Allah," he said, "the Merciful, the Loving-Kind, Whose pity is without bounds! I give this corpse its life! I breathe a human soul into this dog. We are the warriors of Allah! And no vile dealing shall sully our hands. As I pardoned the German that he might gather the dung of my horse, and made him my syce; as I pardoned the white virgin, the Roumi shall live, and as it

[152]

is fitting that a Christian virgin should be mated with a dog, let the Mad Cadi be called, and may the Mad Cadi join the Christian woman and the dog together before Satan, and let my new syce lead them to their bridal chamber in the stable!"

The Mahdi, wanting to preserve Ulysses and the paper above all things, had decided that the marriage would amuse his warriors, and rectify the unpopularity of his unaccustomed clemency.

Baron von Slatin and Sister Agnes were brought. The marriage took place there and then. The Mad Cadi pronounced over Ulysses and the Franciscan nun all the insults, imprecations, and curses of Islam. He spoke at length of all the forms of mating that his imagination, overheated by long abstinence in the sun-parched desert, could suggest to his disorganized brain. He spiced his nuptial blessing with gestures of the wildest obscenity, and a continual hail of laughter disarmed the anger of the dervishes, and they underlined the Mad Cadi's most savorous inventions with lecherous pleasantries of their own.

In this way Ulysses was granted not only his life, but a wife. Baptized by a mad pope, he was married by a still madder cadi.

When Slatin had installed them in the stables, Ulysses declared to Sister Agnes that she had nothing to fear, and that he would respect her vow of chastity. Knowing that he was a heretic, and having a truly apostolic and Roman disdain for the Greeks, she was astonished at his words and did not at first believe them. She believed rather the assurance of Slatin, who, from his long oriental experience, knew the Greeks well; and who, having been first a Jew, and then a Catholic, seemed more worthy of belief. The parable of the prodigal son often has similar paradoxical applications in the Catholic tradition. The converted Jew, whatever the motives of his conversion have been, will always rank higher than the Christian by birth and tradition but of a condemned communion. Prompted by the good sister, they knelt down all three, and thanked the Lord Who had preserved their lives. For a long time the sister could not forgive Ulysses for making the sign of the cross from right to left while she and the Jew made it from left to right. Ulysses swore by all that was holy that his was the right way, and this remark deeply troubled the nun's conscience and drove her to suspect that the Greek was not only a heretic, but a Freemason to boot. She confided her horrible suspicion to her co-religionist, who, being, though she never suspected it, a Freemason himself, tried all the signs on Ulysses. As they caused no reaction, Ulysses issued guiltless from the ordeal. Without asking how he had been put to the test, the good sister was gladdened in heart. It would have been really painful for her to be forced to cohabit with an initiate of the lodges.

On the morrow, Ulysses was called before the Mahdi. He gave him the cheque he had received from the British General Staff. For the first time, the prophet learned the secrets of banking and credit, for, from a practical point of view, divine revelations are not always sufficient. They often leave to the devil the trouble of revealing certain processes, which, useful though they may be, are foreign to eternal salvation. Thus the Mahdi gratified Ulysses by a pat on the shoulder and the epithet "Shaitan." Hearing himself dubbed "Satan," Ulysses concluded that his action had found favour with the representative of God on earth.

As it was the time for midday prayer, Ulysses left the prophet alone and told his companions of his interview. The nun rendered thanks to the Blessed Virgin, and Slatin to the astuteness of the Greeks. But the Greeks received as many thanks as the Blessed Virgin when Ulysses unbuckled his belt and produced the thousand pounds in gold that had escaped confiscation. All day he worked with Slatin, digging a hole for the treasure, while Sister Agnes kept watch on the outskirts of the stables. In the presence of the daughter of St. Francis of Assisi, the two men vowed not to use the treasure except for the good of the community or to facilitate the escape of one or all of them after they had parleyed together.

Thanks to Ulysses' fortune, the little Christian community of Khartoum was supplied with funds and could look upon the future with comparative confidence. It was premature to discover any precise grounds for hope, but despair no longer seemed an integral part of their captivity.

A few days later the community was saddened by a brutal sight: Slatin came home with drawn cheeks, heaving chest, and mangled feet, having run for fifteen miles before the Mahdi's carriage. Sister Agnes tended him all night, and Ulysses groomed the horses and washed the carriages.

For several months, all that Ulysses did was to help the syce in his stable and Sister Agnes in the kitchen work, which was not over-burdensome, as it consisted only of grinding a little of the stable barley into flour every day. On this diet, the community grew rapidly thinner, and Ulysses suggested exchanging the barley for dried dates, which would introduce some variety into their fare. He met a dervish who agreed to the bargain, but accompanied it by such a heavy blow on the back with a hippopotamus-hide whip that Ulysses staggered home in a daze and from that moment renounced all his crazy gastronomic ambitions.

Every day, Slatin ran in front of the Mahdi, who seemed possessed by a demon of activity. He would ride for many miles on horseback or in his carriage, and Slatin's feet gradually formed a natural sole, so tough that a razor would have had difficulty in cutting it. Sister Agnes, who did not know that "the function forms the organ," as the impious Darwin says, cried a miracle, for which she gave thanks to God in her numerous daily prayers. In the same way that Slatin's future safety depended on his feet, Ulysses felt that his depended more and more on his tongue. He had

[156]

profited by the Egyptian Army to master the subtleties of English, of which till then he had known only the jargon of the private soldiers, while from Sister Agnes he learned French and Italian. Later on he started German, which Slatin taught him out of Heine's poems, which he possessed in a small pocket edition. In this way Ulysses began to be a master of tongues.

But these purely literary occupations, flattering as they were to the thirst for knowledge that burns in the breast of every Greek, could not remain the sum of Ulysses' activity. The monotony of study and of their little domestic tasks disgusted him. Sister Agnes, who was a woman by nature and contemplative by calling, supported it with ease. She countered Ulysses' complaints with all the classic lessons of Christian resignation, saying that the soul's welfare was safer in retreat and inaction. Slatin pointed to his hardened feet and his meagre body, envying the Greek's immobility, which he declared far preferable to his own daily courses before the Mahdi's chariot.

In spite of all this wise counsel and the envy that his leisure excited in his fellows, Ulysses chafed in captivity. However much Slatin pointed out to him that his inactive obscurity delivered him from many dangers, Ulysses dreamed of adventures, of buyings and sellings, and of a thousand bold but fruitful combinations. To relax himself commercially he began kneading a little straw gathered from the stables with the offal that the horses provided in such abundance. He moulded cakes

[157]

of it, which, after baking in the sun, are the only fuel of the Nile Valley.

Balancing a pile of cakes on his head, oriental-fashion, he started running around the quarter singing the charms of his merchandise. The first day earned him several handfuls of dates and even a few potatoes. The second day, an old shrew seized them all for nothing, and, when he protested, threatened him with the anger of her husband if he said another word. At his third venture, a vertical scimitar stroke clove all his cakes in two, and only the toughness of his crown saved his skull from a like fate, diverting the stroke towards his right ear, which was nearly severed. Sister Agnes had to wash and dress the wound, reminding her patient all the time of the spiritual and bodily dangers of cupidity. But what weighed heaviest upon him was the Mahdi's silence. He felt himself forgotten. He had believed that the cashing of the cheque, and the explanations that he had given, would have drawn the Master's attention to his great financier. It seemed to him that the prophet was lacking in perspicacity, and letting a valuable chance slip by, in doing without his services. The man of God, in his eyes, seemed too cut off from the things of this world. So he had to resume his study of modern languages, and drowned himself anew in irregular verbs and unusual pronunciations.

The progress of Ulysses was brilliant, and when she heard him express himself in the gentle Italian of St.

[158]

Francis, Sister Agnes began to hope for his eternal salvation. She made him learn several *Fioretti* by heart and, when she heard him repeat them, Ulysses seemed less of an unbeliever to her. The only discordant note was still the sign of the cross, which, at evening prayer, and in his moments of anguish, he still made backwards. Whenever he represented the cross's horizontal beam by moving his fingers from his right shoulder to his left, the nun looked upon it as a sure token of damnation. But Ulysses was unshakable. None of the sister's remonstrances, however gentle, or the Austrian's arguments, which were principally based on reasons of solidarity and opportunism, could convince him. Following the tradition of all Greeks since, and even before, the Photian schism, Ulysses steeled himself against the influence of the Vatican, of whose existence he was not even aware, but which some interior ancestral revolt revealed to him as mysteriously puissant, and dangerous to Hellenism. Ulysses' sign of the cross introduced, into the life of the little Christian community of Khartoum, just that element of theological fury which has so often changed the face of the world and of history.

Quite soon, however, something happened. A giant dervish, with a scimitar slung around his neck on a scarlet lanyard that barred his chest like the grand cordon of some bloodthirsty order, came to find Ulysses, and led him before the Mahdi. There was something

[159]

about his scimitar, his warlike eyes, and his savage bearing that drove Sister Agnes to fall on her knees in prayer.

As soon as he was in the Mahdi's presence, Ulysses beheld Osman Digna, the lieutenant of Tokar, standing by the Conqueror's side. He felt that he had a delicate game to play. His departure from Tokar, his manœuvres in the Red Sea, and the sambouk with her rudder blocked, threatened uncomfortable explanations. Marko's name would help him, unless he had fallen into disgrace, and Ulysses had heard no news of him for months. Osman Digna conducted the inquiry himself, and it was severe, precise, and manifestly malevolent. Ulysses was called upon to account for every one of his actions. But Osman Digna, though a good soldier, made a poor prosecutor. He talked too much, too often interrupting his discourse with benediction or invective. Ulysses soon realized that Marko was superficially in disgrace with the Mahdi, but in high favour with his lieutenant. Above all, he gathered the knowledge that the sambouk had never reappeared in Tokar. But what froze the blood in his veins was the news that one of his desert recruits, who had disappeared on the last day, had revealed Ulysses' Anglophile intentions to Osman Digna. The sambouk having disappeared, Ulysses covered her captain with ignominy. For Marko he had nothing but praise. This seemed to mollify Osman Digna. As for the Mahdi, he exalted him into the seventh heaven of glory. In spite of everything, however, his revictualling of the English remained patent and unobscured, a fact for which the giant's scimitar could at any moment obtain justice. Once more Ulysses' head depended on a gesture of the Mahdi, on the capricious impetuosity of the tropical character. Ulysses had to play his last card. From a word let fall by Osman Digna he had realized that the latter's presence in Khartoum was due to a disagreement with the Mahdi over the sharing of booty. Ulysses became eloquent.

"By Allah! in Whom just justice, and equitable equity, and strong strength reside! There is no misunderstanding between your lordships and my humility! The besieged needed supplies; he took Ulysses' oxen. May Gehenna engulf the man who said that I delivered them of my own free will!—and his mother, and the father of his mother, and his grandfathers, great-grandfathers, and those who first begat his accursed race! May his house fall to the ground! May his women be barren, and his generation die away! The besieger needs no cattle, by the grace of Allah the Merciful, the Loving-Kind! His are the plunder, the precious stuffs, the women, the arms, the horses, and, above all, the gold that gladdens the conqueror's eye. If I have kept gold for myself, if any gold be found upon me, may my head roll at your feet, may my mother be defiled by a donkey, and may the bones of the father of my mother be pasture for jackals. The gold I could have had . . ."

In tallying the plunder, the Mahdi had forgotten to mention to his lieutenant the fortune that Ulysses had surrendered to him. In Ulysses' peroration, he divined a hint of embarrassing revelations. The words of the Greek were as swift as lightning, and sharper than the keenest scimitar. Before it fell, his head, enthroning its precious tongue, might cost more than it was worth.

"My son, silence," interrupted the Mahdi, "thy heart is pure in the eyes of Allah. They that speak against thee, may their tongues rot. Thou art Marko's nephew; my benevolence is upon thee."

Ulysses' head remained upon his shoulders. The Mahdi had decided that in that position (the only normal one, besides) it could render him services that he would lose by detaching it.

When Ulysses returned to his comrades unescorted, the good nun was still deep in prayer. Seeing him hale and unscathed, she ended with an act of grace, and when Ulysses began to boast of his astuteness, exaggerating the subtlety of the reasoning and tactics that had saved his head, she reminded him that he owed his life entirely to divine compassion. Ulysses agreed without demur. He declared that the All-Holy loved him and that his patron St. George had always looked on him with favour, and added:

"But it is nice to have a cat. . . ."

The good sister and the baron thought that his terror of the Mahdi must have turned his brain. He explained that in Greece, when a sailing boat is plagued with rats, a pope is called, who intones the special prayers appointed for the occasion, and sprinkles the hold with holy water, but, before taking his leave, advises the crew to get hold of a cat. . . .

Sister Agnes saw in this parable the notorious inferiority of the Greek heresy, affirming that Catholic prayers would succeed without the cat. Ulysses, whose arrogance had been revived by his fresh triumphs, retorted:

"Please God that we come to no harm! But, should that happen, you will see, my sister, that a cat is always useful; and that, of us three here, I am the cat."

The Arab must be struck while he is hot, like iron; while he is still malleable, one must forge and hammer circumstances that promise future profit. If the moment passes, and no definite advantage is drawn from it, the succeeding moment is generally of evil augur.

Ulysses' brain was bubbling over; he could neither sleep nor sit still. He strolled up and down, turning over a thousand impossible schemes in his head in the hope of finding one small practicable plan.

Lying in the corner, Slatin unrolled a large sheet of yellow, greasy, and fly-blown paper, crossed and recrossed by many folds forming squares like those of a chessboard.

"What are you doing there?" asked Ulysses.

"I've got to escape from this hell, and I am studying a map of the Sudan that I always carry hidden on me."

"And what's that paper for?"

"It is a paper that guides us in war time."

Ulysses squatted beside him and made him explain the mysteries of cartography, scales and distances. He was delighted to discover towns that he knew: Suakin, Tokar, Omdurman, Khartoum, the Nile's course, and the point where he had delivered his cattle to the English.

"Friend, would you mind if I became the Caliph's intimate adviser?"

"Of course not."

"Then give me the paper."

"Why, what is your scheme?"

"Ulysses has a secret, and Ulysses' secret loses all value if it is revealed, even to his brother."

Armed with the paper, Ulysses went straight to the Caliph's quarters. He was in council with his emirs, and sat with feet crossed on a low, table-like stool against the wall. He was presiding over six emirs, who squatted on the ground listening to the Master, who was preaching rather than discussing. At the right moments, they bowed their foreheads and murmured: "Aï nam!"—"Even so!" Although he provoked objections, they were not brought forth, for with the Caliph discussion was permitted, but dangerous. The emirs preferred prudence and agreement to rashness and argument. They knew full well that the tongue that is not for ever honeyed with flattery risks being cut out; and that the head that fails to nod assent does not remain long upon its shoulders.

Pushing the guards aside, Ulysses broke into the middle of the council.

"Lord! I bring you victory!" he cried, waving the unfolded map that flapped behind him like a banner. Without taking breath he knelt down before the Caliph, spread out the map on the ground, and said:

"Master of the Sudan, and tomorrow of Egypt! Here is the Sudan, here is Egypt, and here is the river, and here is Bahr-el-Ghazal and the Kordofan. And here is the heaven-blessed place where your lordship was born!"

The Caliph and the emirs were all leaning over the map now, following Ulysses' forefinger, which was pointing out hills, towns, and valleys. Each one asked for the name of the village whence he came.

"By the name of Allah, the Roumi knows everything!" cried the Emir of the Beri-Jerarts. But the Caliph, skilled strategist that he was, was more interested in distances than localities.

"My son," he said, "all the world knoweth that which thou knowest. If thou answerest my question, we will believe in thy paper. How many hours' march is it from the well of Aïn-Hamid to the well of Hammadia?"

"Running like a syce, or walking before a camel laden with two hundred kantars?" asked Ulysses prudently.

"Walking behind a camel laden with two hundred kantars," decided the Mahdi, after a pause.

[165]

Ulysses had previously studied the proportion of each of his fingers to the scale of the map. He made successive juxtaposed applications with his forefinger, progressing in this way from the setting-out point to the destination. The distance was nine forefingers broad. He divided it by the speed of three miles an hour, but was not quite sure of his method; and, uneasy at the importance of his answer, he stammered:

"From the well of Aïn-Hamid to the well of Hammadia . . . it is three hours on foot . . ."

"By Allah, thou speakest truth!" exclaimed the Mahdi, "thou knowest a road that thou hast never travelled!"

For several hours, Ulysses calculated many distances. He pointed out where the sun rose and set in each town. He named the mountains and oases, and the marvelling emirs interrupted him with exclamations and praise. The Caliph was already proud of his protégé.

"My brother-believers!" he cried. "Is it not written in the Book: 'I shall speak to you also through the mouth of an unbeliever'?"

As they were all of them warriors, they richly appreciated the utility of the map in their future operations.

An emir who knew how to read and write and who had passed twenty years at the university of El Azhar in Cairo, declared that he also understood measurements, and that he could use the map as well as Ulysses.

Ulysses challenged his skill. The journey to be calculated was chosen by the Caliph, in a region that was known to the Caliph but unknown to the emir. The emir repeated all the operations of Ulysses. Like him, he measured with his forefinger. Ulysses, with arms akimbo and full of assurance, signalled to the Mahdi that there would be an error, an enormous error. When the emir announced the result, it was greeted by a universal guffaw. The number of hours was four times too large. The Arab's index-finger had the slenderness of all Arab hands and he had not taken into account the windings of the footpath through the hills indicated on the map.

The university of El Azhar became the object of unfavourable commentary, and the learning of Ulysses was accepted beyond question.

The Caliph clapped his hands, summoning a slave.

"The Roumi must stay with me always. He shall abide in the selamlik!" and, taking the map, he dismissed his councillors, leading Ulysses to the room where all that he prized lay hidden. Drawing an enormous key from his bosom, he opened an iron chest with strong iron bands and a rusty lock. He put the map inside and relocked the chest, which, with Ulysses' help, thenceforward assured him of the knowledge of places, directions, and distances: the path to victory. After this, he not only swore by the Book, as is customary among the Moslems, but sometimes by the Great Paper too. The map became a cabbalistic amulet, of which Ulysses alone possessed the key, to the glory of the prophet and his own advancement. Living in the great palace he became the master of the Great Paper; but, also, its slave.

12

❁❁

*A*FTER his death, the Mahdi was succeeded by the Caliph Abdullah. The new prophet paid Ulysses the signal honour—to him alone among all the unbelievers —of demanding his vow of fealty. Ulysses gave it without surprise. In his own mind he substituted the God of the Christians for the God of the Prophet. Together with the Caliph, and the Emirs of the Black Banner, on whom Abdullah relied to keep him in power, Ulysses chanted:

"In the name of Allah the Merciful, the Loving-Kind, Whose pity hath no bounds! In the name of the One God, we render to God, to His Prophet, and to thee, our faith. We swear that we will attribute to God no foreign thing, neither will we steal nor commit adultery, nor lead our neighbour to deceit, nor disobey the commands that thou shalt give us of thy goodness; we swear to renounce the world, to look only towards the life to come, and to continue the Holy War."

To put his conscience at rest, he added to himself in

Greek: "May the devil take you, and your faith!"

This oath of fealty classed Ulysses among the highest dignitaries. At every sign of disdain, of which there was no dearth, he would say: "I took the oath!"

Sometimes his peers admitted this incontestable proof, and answered: "In the name of God! So be it!" But others, in higher favour at court, or freer in their way of thinking, would answer:

"Dog of a Christian! May thy house fall to the ground, and thy oath choke thee!" So that in spite of his vow and the honours conferred upon him, Ulysses' position was always an unstable one.

It became still more so when the new Caliph, who was more detached from Heaven than his predecessor and prophet, appointed Ulysses financier-in-chief of the Beit ul Mal, the House of Government. This action could not but be unpopular. When the emirs reproached him with appointing an unbeliever to a post in which he would have to collect the taxes of the faithful and see to the upkeep of the mosques and other pious foundations, Abdullah, compromising with his conscience, argued the good fortune they had had, to be able to leave the money question to an unbeliever, who could perform more productive negotiations than those which the Book permitted to the faithful, and the profits of which would lighten their taxes.

Ulysses' first plan was to build an elaborate mausoleum over the body of the Mahdi. His successor greeted this project coldly. He was less afraid of the expense, which would, after all, be paid by his subjects, than of the prolongation of his predecessor's prestige, which he deemed useless, and even harmful.

But Ulysses explained that only the dead are no longer to be feared, and that it was fitting to exploit them against the living, which is the very essence of religion and empire. Glory is more solid when it is founded on tombs; and the more magnificent the tombs, the greater the glory they propagate. Abdullah was easily persuaded, and Ulysses watched over the labour himself. Instead of the Sudanese *turbé*, a modest white cube, Ulysses dreamed of a real temple. Directing the masons, he created, without knowing it, a monument that had as little resemblance to a mosque as the Arab style to the Byzantine, so great is the truth that no man escapes his ancestors. When the mausoleum was finished, the Caliph, the emirs, and the faithful marvelled at a construction that they had never dreamed of being possible, and whose more than human beauty they had never even imagined. They spoke of divine intervention and believed that the angels themselves had set their hands to the mouldings. The Mahdi and his architect did nothing to destroy this legend as, for one, this angelic collaboration was a sign of heavenly favour, and, for the other, the angels' salary richly compensated for the hurt to his professional pride. For his successor, the first Mahdi's tomb was a new power, and for Ulysses, the foundation of a fortune.

As legend had it, the angels worked only at night, and as Ulysses was seen working all day, a certain reflected glory was shed upon him. In council, the emirs would often say to the Mahdi:

"By Allah, thy Roumi is a treasure for the faithful."

But a temple is not enough to keep a country and its finance minister alive. Vaster schemes were ripening in Ulysses' head, and one evening he revealed them to the Mahdi.

"Lord, thou hast conquered. The time has now come for buying and selling. We Roumis, we do not know how to conquer, but buying and selling understand we better than any other tribe. May the sword of the Prophet give way before the kalem of the merchant."

Unfolding the Great Paper, and pointing out what regions produced what merchandise, and mentioning those of which they stood in need, he indicated routes and distances. Buying prices were compared to selling prices, and, when he saw the light of cupidity burning in the Caliph's eyes, Ulysses asked permission to organize these exchanges and set the commerce in movement, ending with the words:

"Lord, thou hast conquered! Plunder in war time is the warrior's delight. In peace time the tithe tax adds its sorrow to the lack of plunder, and sorrow is a bad counsellor. Through trade and its profits, thou canst diminish and even suppress the tithe. The faithful will sing thy praises, instead of complaining in the bazaars, where caliphs are made and unmade. And if ever (which God forfend!) the Evil Hour strike, and the English (may their houses crumble!) attack thee, the faithful will defend thee to defend their own welfare, and the welfare of a town is worth all its battlements! Besides, in my scheme, we will be able to buy cannons and rifles without the help of the men who will use them. For the weapon that the warrior has had to buy himself falls lightly from his hands."

Abdullah underlined his finance minister's last words with liturgical acquiescence. He rose, turned towards Mecca, and prayed the prayer of the Prophet. Having received inspiration from the east, he said:

"My son, do as thou sayest; thine are the key and the seal. But first repeat the words that I shall say to thee:

"*In the name of the One God! And of His Prophet and of my Lord Isa, and our Lady Mariam, I shall keep for myself a hundredth part of the revenue, and I shall give to my lord and my master, Abdullah-el-Taishi, and to none other, and shall faithfully keep for him and none other, all the rest; and should I do otherwise, let first my right hand, and then my left foot, be smitten off, and my wounds be anointed with salt and vinegar, till it shall please my lord of his un-bounded compassion to cut off my head.*"

Having tied him by this oath, where the Christian

God and His Holy Mother were linked with the Prophet to guarantee the swearing, together with the terrible retributions to be suffered in this world, Abdullah laid the key and the seal in Ulysses' hand.

First, Ulysses used the English cheque to start an account at Manchester. He ordered white cotton clothing, which was in high favour with the Negroes, to exchange it for ivory from the Congo basin and the equatorial provinces. He reforged his links with Marko, who was still living by the Abyssinian frontier. His mind dallied with a great scheme in those parts. When he revealed it to the Mahdi, the prophet kissed him on either shoulder, an undreamed-of honour for an unbeliever.

A black merchant from Sennar, who had crossed Abyssinia, had told him that in that strange country they drank hydromel out of drinking horns. Ulysses meditated ripely and decided that each pair of horns represented a head of cattle, which seemed unreasonable. "Κερατάδες!" he cried. "Hornwearers! If it is horns you want, horns you shall get!"

He ordered a hundred thousand horns from Birmingham, made of tin, and each an exact replica of a bull's horn. He ordered black horns, white horns, two-coloured horns. An immense supply was delivered, and Marko's caravans swamped Abyssinia, and, in a short time, only the Negus, the court, the great Rases, and a few of the influential nobles drank out of real horns.

[174]

The lower orders, the masses, all drowsed themselves with hydromel out of the tin horns invented by the Mahdi's financier. The scheme was well carried out. The natives living on the banks of the Blue Nile, of all the Ethiopians the most backward and savage, did not use Maria Theresa thalers in their buyings and sellings. They still paid in kind. The agents of Marko and Ulysses offered them twelve horns for an ox. Seeing that only two horns, sometimes only one sound one, grew on the heads of their oxen, they exchanged immense herds of cattle against these counterfeit horns. The slyness of the savage is hasty and unlimited. Thinking to deceive the Greeks, they wanted to deceive them thoroughly, and they were late in realizing their folly. While the Sudan became full of oxen, they soon began to grow scarce in Abyssinia. The administration of the Negus had to forbid the exportation of cattle to the Sudan, but the plan had already yielded its fruit. Thereafter, Ulysses was pleased with a reasonable profit.

After this magnificent display, the position of Ulysses was beyond all discussion. The emirs greeted him as only true believers are greeted:

"Salvation to thee!"

And Ulysses was allowed to answer:

"To thee salvation!"

This put the Christian dog on a footing that was socially and spiritually equal to that of the Moslems, whose eternal salvation is assured by the Prophet, and who are the only aristocracy recognized in this world by their leaders.

Ulysses profited by it to lighten the loads of his companions, upon whom the Evil Hour had come. He obtained that Slatin should run no more before the Mahdi's horses barefoot. He was allowed to run in sandals. For Sister Agnes he obtained the freedom of the Mahdi's harem, and a modest but clean dwelling on the banks of the Nile at Omdurman. The other Greeks, instead of being concentrated and watched, were all enrolled in his service. He spread them everywhere as his agents, drawing them in the train of his ascending fortune. He placed them especially in the midst of tribes that were allied to the Mahdi, telling them to keep an eye open, and even, as the Greek expression runs, to have "fourteen eyes." In public conferences before the Mahdi, he exhorted them to the most devoted loyalty to their master, whose mercy was their only right to live. In their more intimate councils, held in Greek, he advised them to keep the British reconquest of the Sudan always in mind.

"The hour will come," he told them, "when the devil will take this Mahdi and his horned faith. So we must be ready. Whenever you have a chance, sound the feelings of the emirs at whose courts I accredit you. Praise the Mahdi exaltedly, but if he is insulted, let the insult pass without comment. Repeat frequently that he is very rich and very powerful, and that to become richer and more powerful still, he would trample on his mother's corpse. Always end by saying: 'May Allah shield him with His holy protection!' Be wary and sleep little. This country is destined for the English, and what you now see cannot last. These knaves will be swept aside; we must join in the sweeping. Above all, never write to me; never communicate with me save through the people I send you, and do not confess this that I tell you even to your pope at shrift, or the devil will take your fathers. Go towards the good!"

Such were the orders of the Mahdi's financier. They were always obeyed.

The Mahdi, too, had nothing but praise for the services of Ulysses. For the first time in Islam, the scribes, squatting on their bundles of papers, flicked the nimble beads of their kalems in accurate reckoning. Debit and credit were meticulously established. The scratching of their reed-pens on their rough paper propagated a rustle of efficiency, and as the files swelled with new papers, the scribal seats grew higher. When asked for a deed of sale or purchase, or a koranic reference on a point of law, they could always lay their hands on it with the aid of the date and the height of their seats.

This way of filing archives is not universally practised, but seems the only possible one for the scribes of Islam. Ulysses, besides, had little to do with this documentation. It sufficed him to look at them now and then, with the help of his infallible intuition where

[177]

figures were concerned. Once, when he denounced an unfaithful scribe to the Mahdi, the double-dealing servant had his hand cut off.

Ulysses was not bloodthirsty. He slept uneasily for several days after this, and vowed to be gentler another time. He revealed his thoughts to the Mahdi.

"Lord," he said, "in the matter of the scribes, thy law is not good. If thou continuest to apply it, there will be no more scribes left. Few of thy subjects can handle a kalem, and only with their right hand. If the hand be cut off for the slightest transgression, who will keep the accounts?"

"Thou speakest truly," replied the Master. "Their left hands shall be severed. . . ."

"The hand that they hold their papers with?" objected Ulysses.

"May Allah wreck thy household! Thy tongue is swifter than the mare of the Prophet! I shall cut off both their feet."

Seeing that the clemency of the Mahdi would lead him to behead them outright, Ulysses gave the conversation a new turn.

"Lord," he said, "art thou satisfied with thy servant?"

"As long as the slave is alive, the satisfaction of his lord is manifest," replied the Mahdi.

Ulysses realized that this lesson in humility meant that the Mahdi was satisfied even to the point of fearing that his servant's pride would become overweening; so Ulysses attacked the real question.

[178]

"Sprung from a distant tribe beyond the sea, I would fain die and be buried in the empire subdued by thy good works. Besides, land holds a man faster than honours and gold. Wilt thou give me land, that I may plough and sow it and water it with the sweat of my brow till my grave be dug therein?"

"What land dost thou want?" asked the Mahdi.

Ulysses' choice had been made long ago.

"That which lies near to thine own on the Gezira, that island blessed of God between the two rivers."

"It is thine, son of a dog," the Mahdi answered, smiling. "May it be said that my power is so great that I can give the Prophet's own land to an unbeliever. Draw out the *hodjet*, write the boundaries to north, to south, to east, and to west, so that they be beyond question. I will seal it with my seal, blessed by the Prophet Himself, and may thy land be heavy with barley during thy lifetime, and may it rest lightly upon thee after thy death. So be it."

Ulysses kissed the two hands of the man of God, and became, after him, the greatest landowner in the Sudan. The agricultural sense was poorly developed in Ulysses; but he wanted to assure a fortune that the English would respect, in reward for the services that he meant to render them. As for his fortunes in goods, money, and merchandise, he knew that, on the day of strife, all would be confiscated, lost, and brought to nothing. Under the regime he served, of which he was the living paradox, he needed several strings to his bow,

[179]

for in the desert, more than anywhere else, those strings risk breaking. Above all else, he needed several heads, so difficult did it seem, in the long run, to keep the one he possessed securely on his shoulders. Every day he saw the heads of others falling around him, and he had often watched the bodies of yesterday's favourites swinging from the gallows in the main square, or their heads, the faces frozen in a rictus of terror, rolling in the dust beneath the executioner's sword, to deck the Mahdi's gateway, or serve as a football for the urchins of Omdurman.

Death gnawed at him on every side. He saw it everywhere. His master's messengers left the palace every day on some far mission to a distant chieftain who had grown too powerful or whose fidelity was doubted, returning with a severed head, which they laid at the feet of the prophet, in proof of orders faithfully obeyed. Every day the *ombaya*, that immense death-heralding drum, summoned the population of Omdurman to the great square. When the preparations for the torture were all in order, the Caliph and his court proceeded to the square, and watched the slow work of death, surrounded by the cheers of the people.

Ulysses was living in a reek of corpses and decay. Despite the confidence that the Caliph showed in him, he never abandoned his suspicions, and often his head depended only on a clever answer to an insidious question. He had acquired an unconquerable dexterity in this art on which his life depended. He outplayed the

Mahdi's ambushes with a flux of adulation and ambiguous expressions that could checkmate the most outright question; but in spite of everything, he felt that death was lying in wait for him. Often would he envy the simple prisoners who lay arotting in their filth, but who were not directly under the Master's eye. The humble fellow-countrymen in his service whom he helped in every way within his power, seemed happier than he, for he alone guaranteed their fidelity, their slightest word and deed. The flight of one, the error of another, the slightest real or apparent disloyalty, would set the deadly ombaya beating for him. He knew that the Mahdi would watch his agony with still greater relish, thinking of the long and fruitful service he had reaped from him. Ulysses' life was a dream of riches, and a nightmare of heads severed from their trunks, abominable tortures, and mutilations, in which the blood-greedy imagination of the master of his destiny ran riot. He had to follow every by-way in his master's brain, which was diseased with ambition, cupidity, and the poison of a power that was all the more absolute as it declared itself divine. Always must he guess the true intention that lay behind deceiving words; he had to pit himself against a will that was nothing but a trail of sudden whims, each of them contradicting the one of yesterday, and changing utterly before the morrow. The meanest of eunuchs, the lowest of women, any concubine who had once borne his master night-company, could prevail against him. He knew that the

[181]

Caliph, the emirs, and the magnates loathed the influence that he had acquired. Sinuous denunciation surrounded him, and his only guide in this labyrinth was his own spirit, and the precarious well-wishing of a fundamentally evil, fanatical, double-dealing, and ruthless barbarian.

For ten years he had dwelt in the cave of a wild animal that was ready to devour him as it had devoured so many. Of the companions, lieutenants, and collaborators of his first days, none remained. All the heads that he had seen bowing before the Master in council had fallen, one after the other. His invincible astuteness, and the services he had rendered, had, till then, saved Ulysses; but he who knows the game knows that the playing of it must not be prolonged for ever.

13

IN the native quarter of Cairo, the centuries have been kind in their sparing of a certain palace. It is formed by several houses interlaced and falling to ruin, with rooms ill-joined, staircases contradictory, blind corridors, steps leading nowither, and secret passages running under the street to other houses, ending at trap-doors that open no longer. This agglomeration of old walls, decayed planking, silent courtyards where the fountains never play, and halls where the ceiling alone is lighted by a dust-gloomed stained window, dates from the troubled times of the mamelukes. Each jarring strain in its architecture marks some era of a breed of warriors to whose ambitious, destructive, and anarchistic nature it stands witness. It tells of rising fortune, and of sudden ruin; for the mamelukes were massacred to the last soul, by Mohammed Ali, on the day of the feast of reconciliation in the citadel, to which he had bidden them.

Such was the end of that race, which had enlarged

its dwelling for centuries, filling it with booty and engirdling it with ever-stronger battlements. After the slaughter of the men came the rape of the women and the confiscation of the treasures. All that now remained in that house was born of a newer enterprise; carpets, priceless gold-hilted scimitars, graceful ewers of chased and complicated silverwork, glazed earthenware vessels from Persia with their fugitive rainbow colouring, enigmatic icons of Byzantium, oriental enamelwork, illuminated evangels of the Middle Ages, minute Korans of intricate calligraphy, all whispered of heroic and long-vanished eras, when the humblest of slaves, through tireless and unwonted energy, could grasp the empery of the world.

In the mighty halls where the lords of Islam drank deep of old, in the dark recesses where subtle plots were woven and unravelled, in the rooms of the harem that was haunted still with strange delights (where poison and the bowstring were often the last action of violent and ephemeral loves), a man lived alone, a hermit to ambition. He had taken part in the war of 1870 on the French side, as a soldier of fortune. He had been British Consul General in the Turkish provinces; he had made maps of all Cyprus for the use of the British occupation; in company with a partner, he had been in charge of supplies to the British Army. After holding a commission in the Egyptian Army for some years, he had become Sirdar, commander-in-chief. Powerful and silent, with eyes for nothing but his work, he was forging his weapons. He spoke Arabic like an ulema of El Azhar, and he knew all the Koran by heart, and which verse to quote in each contingency. Familiar with all the secrets of body and soul, he trained thousands of lesser men to warfare. He linked the upright tactics of the West with the cunning ways of the East, and the wraith of a plan served him as well as the brilliance of a Prussian parade. His path, perforce, led upwards; and so, with the passage of time, he reached the summit, only bowing his head with the least possible homage before those kings and emperors whence his hail of honours sprang.

His soul, like that of a condottiere, knew no country. He was ready to offer his genius to the power that was the most propitious to his triumph; and, if he was not a renegade, it was only because his native land happened to be the most powerful in the world.

In his Arabian palace, alone among the things that he had collected about him, that reminded him of destinies like his own—of water-bearers who had become Caliphs or of soldiers who had climbed the steps to the throne of Byzantium—he matured his plans, enshrined in the shadow and fore-silence of great events.

His passion for solitude had already astonished the world, and now the world was waiting for some deed that would dim the lustre of all its heralds, for it believed that he was not cast in the common mould. Popular imagination made him even greater than he was.

[185]

His rare visitors retired from his presence bewildered by his unmoving gaze, and by those steel-blue eyes aglitter like those of a wild beast disturbed in the solitude of its lair; and when he spoke, his grave and seldom-sounding voice would lord the silence, ringing from echo to echo. When he stood up, he was like a column capable of supporting a mighty temple, so great was his gift of imperative immobility. Every word he spoke was like an order. Even in questioning he seemed to dictate the answer. He lived and thought alone in halls that had been built for the holding of multitudes. Strong in the myth that represented him, he held the impossible within his grasp. He could turn the easygoing young British officer, that barrack amateur and sports professional, into a grim and hardened warrior, ruthless in his task; of a light-hearted fellah he could make a Prussian guardsman, holding men and circumstances in his able hand.

For Egypt there was only one possible war, the Sudanese war, and Kitchener was to wage it. He was making his preparations. He foresaw and organized everything, ready to unleash his enterprise only when he knew that every event would fall in with his plans. The history of the taking of Khartoum could have been written beforehand in all its detail, including the last charge, infinitely bloody, exclusively theatrical, and, as it was against a surrendered foe, purposeless, but necessary to the picture, to the glory, which, to be complete, calls for a few losses among the victor's troops.

Before he annihilated the Mahdi, he had to annihilate chance: a labour of years. Information began to
accumulate and congeal into corporate form. Superficial understandings were gradually welded into alliances, and a whole system of controls, pressures, sub-
ornments, compromises, recompenses, and menaces,
succeeding, crossing, and confirming each other, inter-
linking and interdependent, assured the realization of
the integral plan. His secret agents were becoming
masters of the Sudan. They were to be found in each
village, at each well and ford, in the mosques, in the
heart of religious brotherhoods, among the Senussites
of Sahara, and among the Bektashites of Cairo. Many
of them bowed before the Ka'bah stone at Mecca, and
the whole Moslem world was aswarm with them, rot-
ten as worm-riddled timber; for they were among the
Mahdi's emirs, among his kinsmen, and among his
womenfolk. Oftener than not, they did not know each
other, but the task of one fitted into his neighbour's
unawares. The actions of one agent in the desert gave
the clue to those of another in India. They communi-
cated with the centre through varied and mysterious
codes. A notch cut with a knife in a tree-trunk, or a
salaam at one of the Khedive's receptions might trans-
mit an elaborate message. To organize his system,
Kitchener himself had lived in a cave in mid-Sudan,
disguised as a Mahdist, and there he had spun the first
threads of the web that was now strung over the whole
face of Islam. Its meshes trapped and devoured all that

chanced upon it, but he alone knew each particular thread, whither it went, and whence it came. Once the victim was in its toils, there was no escape, and all were involved according to the Spider's will. The Mahdi had been encircled. And, when the day came, he would have to fight against all his hostile and wavering tribes, all those who had grievances, and all the others who were gorged with plunder and had nothing more to gain with him.

Though the Mahdi equipped his army like a European one and drilled it in ways of which he knew nothing, but which he deemed of greater expediency, another, from afar, was outplaying his every move. On the great day, the Mahdi's gunmetal was to prove unsound, his powder damp, and his troops, ordered about in accordance with new-learned notions, were to scatter and flee, defeated by their own disorder. The prophet who had conquered Omdurman with a whiff of chosen heroes was to see the same proud warriors fail at the first battle shock, and their leaders and sacred banners routed in advance by the rumour of the desert, by the wind that swept storm-heralding across the sand, by the poison of doubt, and treason. The Mahdi was to fall, before striking a blow, trampled to death by his own warriors. His body was to be an unrecognizable heap, while the victor, to avenge this lost trophy and his years-long striving, was to shell the mausoleum of the first Mahdi to the ground, scatter his dust to the

[188]

desert winds, and his sacred bones to the muddy waves of the river, that age-long creator of fruitful land, and eternal destroyer of conquerors, and prophets, and gods.

14

❖❖

AT the headquarters of the Intelligence Department, the intelligence officers examined the mail with care. No letter was signed with a name, and the only clue to its origin was a number or a cipher. Sometimes these communications were in ordinary letter form, but usually they consisted of a few incomprehensible words scribbled on a twist of paper, hidden in a turban, under a donkey's hide, with only a small scar to tell the tale, or nailed beneath a flat horseshoe. Sometimes the message was nothing but a strip of bark with a cut on it whose meaning was conveyed by the shape and direction of the cut.

All information received was docketed in files, kept strictly up-to-date, and classified by its character and the quarter from which it came. Order sprang from entanglement, illuminating the controlling mind with a thousand indispensable odds and ends of knowledge by a system that was perfectly adapted to its ends.

Daily, on the stroke of noon, the head of the service presented an accurate report to the Sirdar, who checked and annotated it, ordering all discrepancies and information that failed to tally to be looked into immediately.

Kitchener brooked no delay, and he abominated imprecision. After several years' experience, and several reverses when he had discovered that agents whom he had believed infallible were guilty of shallowness or sloth, Kitchener had so adjusted things that Ulysses became the hub of the whole machine. His number, C.47, was always written in red ink, a supreme honour! Father Ohrwalder, and, in due time, Slatin, had both escaped from the Mahdi and told the tale of Ulysses' influence, his position, and the extent of his negotiations. It was well known that all the commerce of the Sudan was in his hands, and that his agents had made themselves indispensable to all the tribes to east and west and south, and if he neglected the Nile Valley northward from Khartoum to the Egyptian frontier, it was because he had no wish to arouse the Mahdi's suspicions. He had explained this to his master.

"Lord," he had begun, in answer to a reproach, "in spite of the great favour with which thou honourest me, in spite of thy confidence in me (of which I am entirely deserving), I am not one of thy people. My soul is thine, but my skin is white, and white men spy out the north. If some other tribe should ally itself with them (may their zaribas be destroyed! may their kine miscarry! may the bellies of their wives be heavy with the offspring of asses!), it is I, Ulysses, thy faithful servant, who will be suspected, if I deal with them. Rather than call down such a suspicion upon me, let my head be smitten off today in the great square of Omdurman! Rather than mingle with the tribes of Wadi Halfa, with the Gihemabs, the Bisharins, the Amrebs, and the Ababdas, tell the drummer to sound the ombaya straight away, and summon the headsman!"

"Go, my son! With the intelligence of the devil, thou linkest the courage of the lion and the cunning of the serpent. . . ."

"Lord! Thy words are not fitting; for I link but devotion with gratitude for all thy benefits."

Thus Ulysses spoke.

"The Emirs of the Gihemabs, south of Wadi Halfa, of the Bisharins and the Amrebs in the south, and the Ababdas north of the El Atbai mountains, are with us. Direct contact with them can be obtained through F.14."

Thus had Ulysses written to the Intelligence Department at Cairo a month before.

He had forbidden his Greeks all contact with these tribes. He had forbidden his Arab merchants, too, to ply their trade in the Nile Valley north of Khartoum, and for months the emirs of the north had been complaining of this neglect. They had brought their grievances straight to the Mahdi, and Ulysses returned dilatory answers to all that was said to him. To the emirs he explained that he had their welfare at heart, and that his only wish was to trade with them, saying that his agents would be dispatched immediately. But he did not hide from them that their situation on the threshold of Egypt necessitated especial precautions that delayed the exchange of merchandise. Finally, he filled them with such appetizing promises that their cupidity was lulled to sleep with satiety, for in the Orient promises are but the euphemistic form of refusal.

Ulysses had reached a cross-roads in his life. For some time the Mahdi had been showering such outstanding favours on him that they began to be an encumbrance. He would even send him the choicest morsels from his own table; and these culinary honours reminded Ulysses of his native land, where the only creatures that are ever fattened are the pig at Christmas and the lamb at Eastertide. This humouring of his appetite hinted the sacrificial axe. So, the swallowing of these meats of honour was hindered by the sensation of a rope tightening about his throat, and by the spasm of his carotid as the scimitar seemed to touch the nape of the neck.

"If he fills me with good things like this," he said to himself, "my death must be already certain. It is only a question of time. Dervishes and your horned religion! As you are fools enough to give me time, it shall work for my good, not for yours, O thick-headed Negroes."

[193]

Each time that a procession of the Mahdi's slaves brought Ulysses the great copper dishes laden with honey cakes, or the most succulent quarters of a roast lamb perched on mountains of rice and swimming in rare sauces, he redoubled his watchfulness and treason. When, three years before, a merchant from Cairo had brought the first news of the work begun by Kitchener, Ulysses had stayed his hand. He deemed the Mahdi's turban more profitable than Kitchener's tarboosh. The easy disorder of the dervishes was more propitious to his schemes than the orderly and indiscreet supervision of the British. Here his talents could unfold themselves in ease, for despotism has always brought prosperity to its principal agents, and of such was Ulysses. But experience had ripened his thought. In the end he understood that arbitrariness may lead one to the highest peaks, if one can but escape in time, so he determined to leave the Mahdi's empire, and by the main gateway, without haste, but with all his luggage. As the gate was locked on the inside, he must help to force it from without. By simple flight he would be letting the fruit of ten years' labour slip between his fingers, but, by flight when he had made smooth the way of the invader, all his goods would be assured and new remunerations gained to boot.

This new game called for the utmost patience, and brought all his resources into play. If success were to be gained, Ulysses would have to surpass himself. Strong in these resolutions, he resorted to the most

[194]

superhuman activity and suppleness. Kitchener said of him, later:

"Without Ulysses, the reconquest of the Sudan would have been, if not impossible, at least much more expensive," and he never knew to the full what odds Ulysses had had to overcome.

He was forced to act with desperate wariness and ponderation, without the slightest hastening of things, and without arousing the smallest suspicion in the breasts of the essentially suspicious barbarians. Whenever he wanted to confide a secret, he had to undermine his confidant, make certain of his discretion, and compromise him so deeply that he had nothing more to fear from him. Often he had to make time, letting precious moments slip by, missing necessary combinations and losing useful support, to adjust himself to the march of things in Egypt. After dispatching urgent information, he had to wait months for an answer, in anguish-fraught inactivity. The more time passed, the deeper he drowned himself in the honour and opulence that the Mahdi bestowed upon him. In the beginning, he had had no other rights but those of a slave whom every man may spurn. He grew richer, but remained obscure and tolerably free in his movements. Gradually, through a whim at first, but later through calculation, the Mahdi forced luxury upon him, putting him before the public eye. As he could not do without him, he did not wish to behead him prematurely. He needed cannons and guns, and Ulysses was

[195]

the only man who could, by roundabout by-ways and the most intricate smuggling, procure them. Forced to let him live and act as he would, the Mahdi held him by the softness of good living, a discreet vigilance, and a constant hail of favours. He placed him so high that every man's eye was upon him. Each month he honoured him with a new *jibbah*—a white linen tunic, woven for the Mahdi alone, and recognizable from afar. It was more than a livery; it was a straitjacket that hampered his every movement. Being the highest honour in the whole Sudan, it excited the envy of all the lesser favourites; and the envy of lesser favourites has always been the first favourite's ruin and the tyrant's security. So the white jibbah burned the frame of Ulysses as the shirt of Nessus burned Hercules of old, and hung upon its wearer's shoulders as heavily as a winding-sheet.

But for some while now the Mahdi had shown a still more embarrassing attention. The better to enmesh and spy upon his favourite, he made him the gift of a wife at each new moon. Sometimes it would be a powerful, cannibal-toothed Negress, sometimes a fiery Abyssinian woman of a pure Semitic type, sometimes a honey-coloured Arab from Arabia. Ulysses' house began to fill with women. He had every kind of woman as concubine: scarcely nubile virgins, worn-out trollops from the stews of Omdurman, lawful wives of whom the Mahdi had wearied, thick-headed slave-girls, and ripe princesses who claimed the luxury and honour due to their noble rank. Ulysses' harem became, after the Mahdi's the best filled in Sudan. The expenditure it involved was considerable, and Ulysses had come to the Sudan to make money, not to spend it on women.

Being but little inclined to venery, he had, till then, known only two or three women, and from each he had reaped considerable advantage. It was through the Alexandrian one that he had got to know the British sergeant and had his twenty-five pounds entrusted to him; and the other in Suakin had indirectly provided him with the two hundred pounds of the Egyptian commandant. To keep women was, thought Ulysses, the opposite of good business. He already had thirty wives, who all wanted to be fed and clad in finery. They demanded bracelets for their arms, and rings for their feet and ears, and even for their noses. They needed perfumes, and paint for their faces, and ointment with which to pile their tresses like domes upon their heads. They picked quarrels with one another on the slightest pretext, screaming insults in all the dialects of the Sudan and the neighbouring regions. In only one thing could they agree: the obloquy they heaped on the accursed and curmudgeonly Nazarene to whom the Mahdi had abandoned them.

The Mahdi rejoiced from the bottom of his heart over the embarrassment of Ulysses. The despot, and above all the oriental despot, relishes any trick that he can play upon his favourite. It is his vengeance for the influence that he allows him. He loves to fill with domestic humiliation the palace that he has bestowed. The contrast seems salutary to him, and, starved of entertainment, he assists with delight at the family dramas of some favourite, with whose every resource and weakness and vanity he is acquainted; for it is only thus that he can enjoy his difficulties and complaints to the full. From Morocco to Lahore, and from Istanbul to Polynesia, a favourite whose wife deceives him is a heaven-sent feast to his sovereign. He unveils his grievances without mercy, chuckling with pleasure at his henchman's complaints of discovered unfaithfulness. He demands to be told every detail, and loses himself in minute and bawdy questioning. The most intimate and lubricious details have to be retold a hundred times, to be recommented upon and dissected with ever-growing enthusiasm. The master cheers the telling with pejorative comments and suggestions. The woes of his favourite are the only book and theatre that the oriental potentate knows; and if those woes are conjugal, the richer the comedy; and the Mahdi was an especial connoisseur in this particular.

Having every reason to please his master, Ulysses readily appointed himself author and producer. Besides, his women made it an easy task. There was no demand they left unsaid, no household scene unplayed. Ulysses cut a poor figure among those followers of the great Mohammed, whose superhuman virility had become a legend, and the little he had was weakened by the preoccupation of filling his pockets and of the calls that were made upon them.

Between these two poles of thought, love (even in its strictly physical form) had so little place that it grew steadily more atrophied. Whenever the eunuchs of the Mahdi presented him with a new wife, he took pains to do honour to his master's gift. But being accustomed to the fieriness of the Mahdi, she always retired discontented. By the first glimmers of dawn, the Mahdi was abreast of all that had happened, and Ulysses, in his daily audience, was forced to endure the most disagreeable criticism. To amuse the tyrant, Ulysses pandered to all his weaknesses. To excuse himself, he attributed his mediocrity in the lists of love principally to spells, the evil eye, or the practices of his harem sorceresses.

These explanations invariably provoked resounding claps of laughter from the Mahdi, followed by more plausible, but always lubricious elucidation. In this way Ulysses wore himself out over the distractions of his master, and the lassitude springing from the tardy advance of his own interests. The Mahdi could well understand all comedy of the Aristophanean kind, and the compatriot of the author of The Frogs could richly satisfy him. Learning through one of his eunuchs that an old princess was deceiving Ulysses with a palace groom, the Mahdi made haste to inform the injured husband.

Ulysses felt it best to display anger and honourable despair. To entertain the man of God, he swore to be revenged on his unfaithful wife.

"By Allah," he shouted, "were I in my own country, only the death of this harlot could avenge my honour; but, being a slave in a foreign land, nothing can wash my face! None of the cadis would punish the erring wife of a Christian dog, of a poor exiled Nazarene!"

At this outburst, the Mahdi's hilarity knew no bounds. He assembled the eunuchs, the cadis, the emirs, and the palace servants to give to Ulysses' performance the spice of a full house. Comment was heaped on comment, every man gave his advice, and the cadis pronounced lewd sentences, describing in detail the tortures that the law inflicted upon an adulterous wife. The court rang with laughter.

Ulysses emerged from this scene with a new jibbah to console him, and two huge tusks in the guise of horns. Having, despite the parody of his obligatory marriages, an instinctive horror of this emblem of conjugal unfaithfulness, he refused the horns, although they were made of ivory and had a certain commercial value.

From all this buffoonery, in which he played his part as best he could, he conceived a cautious hatred for the man who made it necessary. Slowly, his honour as well as his interests was driving him into the arms of the English; and the Greek is really at his best only when he can link what he thinks to be his honour with his certain interests. Being possessed, besides, of a subtle reasoning mind, this alliance does not make him uncomfortable. But the very same day, he regretted the return of his honour, which was given back to him with an exaggeration that was peculiar to the Mahdi.

At the end of the evening meal, to which he had been bidden to the palace as guest, the slaves brought in an immense dish of rice, as usual. When the lid was raised, instead of roast lamb, the guests, doubled up with mirth, saw the two severed heads of the adulterous princess and her groom, side by side in the platter.

The prophet and the faithful fell upon the rice, and congratulated Ulysses on his regained honour. But Ulysses, who was shocked to his very depths, obstinately refused the rice-balls that the Mahdi offered him.

"Eat, thou fool!" cried the Mahdi. "Here is your honour back again!"

But Ulysses preferred his dishonour to the rice of reparation. He found, besides, that death and mutilation were drawing too near to his own person.

During the next few months he intensified his relations with Cairo. He carried out the orders he received with feverish activity. He dispatched his information without a moment's delay. His agents were all on tiptoe, and he constantly advised Cairo to stay her hand no longer, as his position would soon be untenable. All these actions, these goings and comings across the desert, these vessels sailing up the Nile, these long caravans of camels, were explained to the Mahdi as redoubled commercial activity. Ulysses gave no handle to suspicion. More than ever did he work on the replenishing of the Sudanese arsenals with arms. Cairo received exact information on these points. His caravans brought supplies to the tribes but also hid the future supplies of the invaders at fore-determined points. The emirs who were hostile to the Mahdi had all received the word of command, and the details of Kitchener's far-reaching battle plan. Ulysses was waiting only for the signal of evacuation that had been agreed upon: a white camel with a red saddle, the number of tassels on the right indicating the month of Ulysses' flight, and on the left, the exact day of the month. As soon as the camel should arrive, bringing messages to the Mahdi, Ulysses was to arrange, first, the immediate flight of his countrymen, for whom Marko was waiting in Abyssinia, and then his own.

15

✺✺✺

THE white camel with the red saddle had come. Ulysses, on the most plausible pretext, had evacuated his Greeks; and he had only a few days left for flight before the swift and mysterious rumour of the desert should whisper into the Mahdi's ear the news of the Anglo-Egyptian advance.

Kitchener was already at Wadi Halfa. Everything was ready. All that remained was for Ulysses to take his flight. He had to gain a day's march, and twenty kilometres north of Khartoum the swiftest dromedary of the desert awaited him. Once astride it he would be beyond the Mahdi's reach. But, for the moment, he had to bide his time.

His position at court grew more magnificent from day to day, and the Mahdi's vigilance was redoubled. It was impossible to leave the palace without arousing suspicion. Ulysses had attempted it many times, but had always been brought back on various pretexts. The groom who was swift-footed as a galloping horse, the women who watched from far off, and the empty-gazed eunuchs, had all promised the Mahdi to prevent any attempt at escape.

Ulysses was held a prisoner by his glory, by his services, by his wealth, and, above all, by his white jibbah.

There was only one thing left: the real prison, the horrible dungeons of Omdurman. He had appointed a creature of his own as governor of the jail, a camel-man who knew every grain of sand in the desert, and who could run twenty leagues in a day with neither food nor drink. Ulysses would have to fall from the pinnacle of favour into prison. But what could be more difficult for a favourite than to fall into disgrace, without committing an act that would actually endanger his life?

Ulysses came before the Mahdi, to present his daily report. He announced the arrival of six cannons, and the sale of a hundred elephants' tusks at an un-dreamed-of price. He had ordered the chief of the eunuchs to bring him an unclothed virgin who was almost white, and without blemish. Having flattered the warrior, the merchant, and the lover, he enjoyed a long moment of praise and promised reward. Ulysses had culled a long list of complaints against himself from among the countless petitions sent to the Mahdi. He had long kept them hidden. When he showed them to his master, the Mahdi was dumbfounded, and menaced the plaintiffs with all his thunders. He would cut off their ears and noses, and level their houses and tribal zaribas. Ulysses allowed this flood of flattery to

[204]

himself and menaces against his accusers to flow by.

"O well-beloved Master!" he said at last. "Thy heart is too merciful and thy thinking too upright. If I have always served thee well, I will now render thee my greatest service. I am but a Nazarene, a slave, less than the dust beneath the feet of true believers. But the Emir Hassan, who accuses me, is lord of three thousand lances, and the Caliph Abd-el-Ratif, of seven thousand. Abdullah Ibn Saud, who writes three pages of complaint against me, was once an ally of Gordon, and commands the mightiest tribe in the East, and all the others are thy brothers, and thy best warriors. What weight can I have in the balance, should even the least among them be on the other side? Thou art great among the great, thou art strong among the strong, thou art the shadow of God on earth; after the Prophet, thou art the only prophet, and thou alone knowest the full truth of his words. But has it not been said that 'the gadfly may vanquish the mare, a swarm of ants may overcome the lion, and a rat may bring the elephant to naught'? Why shouldst thou displease thy warriors? They are jealous of me. Punish me. They will be satisfied. Later, in a day, a month, a year, according to thy will, thou canst raise me to my pedestal again. The pleasure of my humiliation will console them for a long time for their displeasure at seeing my honours re-established, and they will rest content in the hope of a fresh disgrace, like the one that thou shalt already have imposed upon me. The continuity of thy favours

[205]

is what irks them most. To them, it is against nature, and against the law. Above all, take back the holy jibbah that distinguishes me beyond all bearing in their eyes. Let me don the common galabieh of the water-bearers. That, more than anything, will gladden their eyes, which jealousy eats out like flies in summer. As my punishment is in thy service, let me be well treated in prison. Do not let them weld the ankle-galling fetters upon me, that weigh upon a man's step for the rest of his life; for thy future service, I must be light of foot. Fling me not into a gloomy dungeon. My eye must be clear that I may the better serve thee when the time comes."

Thus was Ulysses thrown into prison. His words had pleased the Mahdi, who admired the sly devotion of his favourite. Since he was heir to the great Caliphs of Baghdad and Cairo, the discomfiture of his vizier followed a tradition that had its roots in his innermost instinct. The wandering tellers of the *Thousand and One Nights*, those sagas of Islam, had too often sung him the tales of similar roundabout cunning, that he should not savour such a plan, and find it a true gauge of the Caliphate he had assumed. But he asked time for reflection. He consulted the ulemas and soothsayers. He summoned a santon to the palace, a limping, louse-ridden old greybeard, with long tangled locks, whose huge skeleton body made him the obvious interpreter of God's will. It was his task to ratify,

[206]

through incomprehensible prophecies, whatever decisions the Caliph had already made in his caliphal conscience. All the Mahdi's advisers were quick to say everything that was expected of them, but to this one he gave the importance of a divine consultation. They adopted the project of Ulysses, turning it into a peremptory command of the prophet of Islam. The scene of Ulysses' degradation, too, assumed a ritual solemnity, for the Mahdi assembled the flower of Omdurman at the palace for the occasion. Ulysses was brought in last of all, and thrown on his knees. He was stripped of his honorific jibbah and his head was bowed for several minutes beneath the maledictions of the Mahdi; each curse was underlined by general approval, and finally he was put into the hands of the chief jailer. Letters drafted in the purest prophetic strain were sent by special couriers to inform the emirs who had demanded his downfall that their behests had been granted. But on the fourth day, the Mahdi sent for him. Without Ulysses, he believed himself lost.

He was lost indeed.

For two days Ulysses and his jailer had been hastening towards Kitchener at the fastest trot of the swiftest dromedary in the desert. The body of a prisoner who had been executed the day after Ulysses' imprisonment had been put in Ulysses' cell, and the real inmate into the coffin. The Mohammedan coffin is nothing but a stretcher covered with a shroud, whence the corpse is thrown into its grave. The first jailer and the chief headsman himself, a gigantic Negro, expressly deaf-mute, to prevent his heart from softening at the shrieks of the tortured, and his possible indiscretion to the detriment of justice, bore the coffin beyond the city walls. As long as they were in the town, the rare passers-by accompanied the convoy for a few moments, intoning the funeral prayers of Islam, and carrying the coffin by turns. The women, forbidden to pray in public, contented themselves with piercing and tremulous wails, produced by the vibration of the tongue against the lips. At certain moments, the shrill fluting of the women, mingling with the deeper chanting of the men, produced such a pleasant harmony, and the coffin changed hands so often, that Ulysses could almost believe himself really dead, and enjoying a high-class funeral. He almost fell asleep, lulled by the swing of the coffin, and, at one moment, believed he heard the *miroloi* of the Greek women in the wakes of his native village. To keep his awareness of life, he incessantly repeated: "Unclean dogs!" to himself in Greek.

When they had passed the town walls, the crowd dispersed, and the coffin was in the hands of the two prison officials once more. When the town was far enough behind them, the sudden resurrection of Ulysses, who quietly got off the stretcher and unwrapped himself from the shroud, struck the deaf-mute with such an access of terror that he let the coffin fall, and took to his heels in the direction of Omdurman, while the jailer and the arisen Ulysses fled to the north, leaving but one witness of their flight, whose silence was beyond question.

16

✪✪✪

IN the palace of Ras El Tin in Alexandria, the Khedive was about to hold his weekly reception. First he would receive the princes of the blood of Mohammed Ali, then the diplomatic corps, then the heads of all the religions practised in Egypt—first, the great Imam of Alexandria, and then, in order of precedence, the Patriarch of Alexandria, the Chief Rabbi, the Catholic Archbishop, the English clergymen, the Orthodox and Catholic Coptic bishops, Armenians, Syriacs, Chaldeans, and the Autocephalous Archbishop of Mount Sinai; the Rector of the Jesuits' college, the Guardian Father of the Holy Land, the Friar Superior, and the Mothers Superior of all the convents and colleges. In a word, the whole Godhead, manifested by the hubbub of its contradictory representatives on earth. Following the dictates of etiquette the Khedive would then receive the general officers of the British and Egyptian Armies, and the bankers and notable Europeans of the country. The whole crowd would congregate in vast halls that were parquetted in pure ebony. The most illustrious would enter by the great staircase, the others by the more modest one leading to the office of the Groom of the Chambers.

All were patiently waiting to be received according to their rank, or the class to which they pretended to belong.

Suddenly, a fanfare of trumpets rang out, the guard presented arms, and Kitchener, heavy and powerful, covered with honours, magnificent in his red tarboosh and the Order of the Osmanieh that hung about his shoulders, slowly climbed the great staircase, preceded by the Grand Master of Ceremonies, and followed by his aide-de-camp. As he was always punctual and could not bear waiting, the Khedive (aware of the haughty impatience of his Sirdar) hastily dismissed the commander-in-chief of the British Army, to receive the Irishman who commanded his own. For him alone would he advance to the door of the throne-room, and Kitchener, full of apparent respect and inner disdain, bowed just as low as was necessary, while the Khedive, full of inner hatred and outward politeness, bowed a little lower than he needed, and led the commander of his army to the throne, and seated him on his right. After a few minutes' conversation, the Master of Ceremonies approached and stood before the throne with his hands folded on his huge stomach, clad in an ill-fitting "stambouline" frock-coat. The Khedive gave the order for Ulysses to be introduced, as Kitchener

[211]

insisted on presenting him to the sovereign himself.

Ulysses advanced among the astonished bankers and important paunchy grocers of Alexandria with complete self-possession. He walked firmly across the slippery parquet, but made his bow too low and too far off when the Khedive offered him his hand. Haunted by memories of the Mahdi, he almost kissed it. As he introduced him, a fugitive gentleness came and tarried a moment on Kitchener's impassive mask.

"Your Highness," he said, "this is Ulysses, who, after your loyal troops, has done more than anybody to give you the Sudan."

The Khedive asked Ulysses to sit on his left and, turning slightly towards him, without daring to turn an inch of his back to Kitchener, said:

"I knew that your fellow-countrymen rendered me great services in trade; I have the highest esteem for them; but I am very happy to meet the one who has helped to give me the Sudan, which my ancestors conquered of old, and which my troops have reconquered."

"Great Prince," answered Ulysses, in a voice accustomed to flattering the mighty, "the glorious general has already been too good to me, but he has crowned his manifold kindnesses in recommending me to Your Illustrious Highness."

Kitchener, in whom, despite everything a grain of Irish humour still lingered, made Ulysses tell the tale of his flight from Omdurman. When he came to the funeral, the Khedive remarked that the soil of the Sudan was, beyond question, too light to keep a devil like Ulysses.

In accordance with the Khedive's etiquette, when he had scarcely left his private audience, Ulysses had to assist at the general one too. It was considered bad taste not to take part in it even if one had been received a minute before.

At this general audience, Ulysses was retained by the sovereign, and seated on his right hand, when all the notables had filed past; for the first time, the president of the Greek community in Alexandria received only the seat on the left of the throne, while the others sat down haphazard on the chairs that were arranged along the walls.

The Khedive, like most monarchs, found great difficulty in relinquishing a joke once he had got hold of it. He spoke for several minutes of the lightness of Sudanese earth, unable to keep such an active corpse. Ulysses and the president of the Greek community roared with laughter; the immediate neighbours of the trio felt obliged to laugh discreetly, and, the core of the assembly showing signs of hilarity, a smile appeared all down the walls, on the lips of those who had heard absolutely nothing. When the Khedive rose, the whole company rose too, and filed past him again. The general audience was at an end.

For five years, Ulysses was a personality; first in the Sudan and later in Egypt. Serving Kitchener as guide and adviser in Sudanese politics, he had re-entered Khartoum with him. It was he who got into direct touch with the allied or friendly tribes that he had won to the English cause. Thanks to him, the victualling of the troops during the march had worked like machinery. When the town was reconquered, Kitchener asked him to find the body of the Mahdi; he searched among the smoking ruins, deafened by the groaning of the wounded and the yells of the fleeing dervishes, but could not find it anywhere. The only things he found were a few shreds of his old master's blood-stained jibbah.

"There is nothing left of the second Mahdi, but there is always the tomb of the first," he had said to Kitchener, pointing out the mausoleum, the work of his own hands. "It must be destroyed."

Kitchener was afraid of public opinion in England. The destruction of the tomb might be taken amiss by the English middle-class politicians.

"General," Ulysses insisted, "I built that tomb, so surely I have a right to destroy it. In Africa, the dead count more than the living, and tombs more than palaces."

Kitchener, who liked simple, sound formulas, approved of this idea, and had it put into action.

Of the terrible reign of the two prophets, nothing now remained, not even a relic. Only the huge, empty spaces were still there, depopulated in ten years by uninterrupted massacres.

All that remained for Ulysses to do was to busy himself in turning his fortune to profit. The lands given and confiscated by the Mahdi before his flight were returned to him. British gratitude bestowed others upon him, supplying the capital to found a limited company, which he launched soon after.

The commercial connexions that he had established under the Mahdi made him, after the British occupation, the master of all Sudanese trade, which was strengthened and fostered by the feeling of security that soon prevailed. His caravans left for the Sudan with cargoes of English cotton wares, and returned laden with ivory. Abyssinian oxen began to till the Sudan once more.

The power of Ulysses became so great that a Russian prince who wanted to hunt big game in the Fashoda district, armed with the warmest British safe-conducts, followed general advice by arming himself in addition with the letters of recommendation from Ulysses for all the tribes of the Upper Nile. They stood him in good stead. For the Negroes swarmed around his tent, and when his interpreter displayed his passport with the great seal of the Sudanese Government, they tore it to pieces and approached still closer with lowered assagais. But when they saw the modest seal of Ulysses, they carried it to their lips and dispersed.

The power of Great Britain was scarcely even guessed at by the most civilized of them, while the power of Ulysses was well known to the wildest.

[215]

But the Sudan proved too small for him. Only the rich valley of the Delta, the great cotton trade and important commerce on a world-wide scale, could satisfy his new ambitions. He shifted his headquarters to Cairo, and cemented his position there at the first brush. Buying a fat bundle of shares, he became a director of the National Bank of Egypt, which had just been founded, in partnership with the greatest Greek and Jewish financiers. Among his powerful compatriots, secure in at least two generations of successful business, and the aristocracy that springs therefrom, he became a "homogenite"—an equal by birth, one of them, a peer, to whom one could give one's daughter in marriage, and who could be honoured by appeals for patriotic subscriptions. This title, the only one recognized by Greek society, follows a fortune made abroad but destined to be spent at home on good works and patriotic subscriptions. Once the title has been given by one's fellow-peers and public opinion, it sticks to one for ever. A homogenite remains such, whatever he may do, and whatever he may have done before, provided that he has not failed to make a great deal of money.

Ulysses earned this title by immediate acts of charity on such a scale that the rumour of them has been handed down the years, to be lost in legend.

The Holy Sepulchre, and its Patriarch, where crippled with debts, which were threatening the fair name of Hierosolymite Orthodoxy. So Ulysses advanced him seventy thousand pounds sterling without interest.

The presentation of the cheque took place with great circumstance at Jerusalem.

The Patriarch, in his archiepiscopal dalmatic, surrounded by an assembly of stoled priests, received Ulysses, accompanied by the Greek Consul in uniform, in the Patriarchal throne-room. While Ulysses advanced to prostrate himself before the old holy man, the choir intoned the canticle:

"Blessed is he that cometh in the name of the Lord."

Kissing the Pontiff's hand, Ulysses gave him his Bank of England cheque and was presented with the Grand Cross of the Holy Sepulchre and the Order of the Holy Saviour, dispatched by the King of Greece. (This cheque, destined to fortify the Holy Sepulchre against Muscovite enterprise, occasioned the recall of the Russian Consul General for incompetence.)

Thus Ulysses' gestures had already acquired international significance.

In the same generous way, he financed the Greek bands that were starting to fight against the all-powerful Bulgarian propaganda in Macedonia. Hundreds of comitadjis paid for Ulysses' fortune with their lives; thousands of Macedonians abjured the exarchist schism and returned to the fold of the Greek Church, because Ulysses willed it so. He worked with all his might *ad majorem Greciæ gloriam*, and became one of the mightiest among the homogenites.

His sisters, who were in service in Athens, were withdrawn from the houses where they worked, richly dowered, and all married inside of a year. He built an enormous house for his mother in Cairo, where she felt quite lost, and could not console herself for the fact that a cook deprived her of the only occupation she cared for, and served her food that always disagreed with her.

Ulysses endowed his native village with a college, to which no schoolboys ever came, and a vast church, which the pious, but scanty parishioners could never hope to fill. Society looks askance if the village of a homogenite has nothing but its elementary school and humble chapel to grace it. More than one little Greek hamlet cowers in the overwhelming shadows of its college and its cathedral.

But people said that, having kept his head with the Mahdi, Ulysses lost it with patriarchs and consuls. So many honours and so much charity drove him to speculation and chancy enterprise. He lost all sense of proportion, buying all shares and all wares, giving with open hands what he thought he had gained, without even keeping his books up-to-date or clearing his debts. Embarrassments were not slow to appear. But his credit was such that no one suspected his difficulties, which made them worse.

So, one day, he found himself bankrupt, with tremendous liabilities.

17

❀✿❀

THE vast halls of the Delmonico Hotel in New York are full of men and women whose clamorous and spasmodic pleasure has grown weary of champagne, crazy rhythm and swamp-haunted moan, glittering lights, pearls that are too fat, diamonds that are too big, throats that are too white, lips that are too red, laughter that is too unbroken. It is a delirium of millionaires who can find no new pleasure to add to the pleasures they have already experimented with. It is the release of minds that are mail-clad for the daily struggle; a struggle without respite, without any other truce than that of Christmastide, the one night in the year when the Anglo-Saxon spirit unbends in contact with an oriental legend. These men and women, whose heads and hearts their prosperity has withered, become children again for a few short hours at the touch of a child in a manger, virgin-born. . . .

The divine child, who dreamed and prayed and died on the cross, had too much kindness in him, that no particle of gentleness should subsist in any human soul. Whatever the world be, whatever it may become, it will never quite prevail against this incommensurable pity. Men will forswear it, deny it, and band against it; but a few scattered shards will always remain, however changed and unrecognizable.

On this night, in the clouds of cigarette and cigar smoke, the wine grows more bitter and the laughter more empty. Strangers shout to one another, tables are confounded, and unlikely paper hats stand or hang in rags on every head, and faces are distorted in drunkenness, mimic, and masquerade.

All at once, twenty young women, all beautiful, all proud in the consciousness of their perfect bodies, streamed into the ballroom. Their dresses were all striped in silver and blue, like the flag of Greece. Their shoulders were as naked as Hymettus, and their arms were like the missing arms of Aphrodite. They swarmed between the tables, seized the cigarettes and cigars from every hand and mouth, extinguished them, and lit other cigarettes, which they drew from their little wicker baskets, strung to their waists on blue ribbons, at the moisture of their lips, and offered them with the words:

"If you love me, smoke 'Ulysses' cigarettes."

Men and women, of every age, enchanted by this dazzling entry, hailed the joke with a compliment to the lovely givers, and Ulysses had launched his brand on the market. His stock was sold out next day. "Ulysses" cigarettes were at once in greater demand than the "Nestors," of old fame. In America, failure often dogs an enterprise step by step down twenty years of constant effort, and success may immediately crown some insignificant idea, provided it be a good one that adapts itself, if only for a moment, to the pleasure- and wealth-blunted taste of the rich.

The idea had penetrated Ulysses' head like a flash of lightning. He had not given it a moment's thought, but all the meagre savings of two years of incessant work had been spent in making it possible.

Landing in New York without a groat in his pocket, after his Egyptian collapse, he immediately presented himself to a compatriot. He knew no one, but following a long, narrow road, he stopped in front of the first shop-front whose superscription had a Greek air, however deformed and anglicized. Pan Voultson, he thought, must surely be a disguised version of Panayoti Voultsos. He was not mistaken. It was a little restaurant that was patronized exclusively by his compatriots and betrayed its nationality by a strong smell of garlic and oil.

"What do you want with me?" asked the landlord.

"Some work, and a slice of bread," Ulysses had answered, according to the formula for all preliminary dialogue between the firmly established immigrant of yesterday and the newcomer of today in search of work.

"I have no work for you," was the fatal answer.

Ulysses stopped at the stall of a certain Charles

Michaelson, formerly Charalambos Michaelides, and another belonging to John Lyonson, which he unveiled as Xenophon Leontidis, with like failure. Again and again he tramped that way of the cross, and each station was a halt that led towards despair. New York seemed to be worse than the Sudan. He passed many foodless days and sleepless nights, and he learned for the first time that imploring look which is flung towards the automaton passing on its way that crushes all before it, with the appearance of a man but the indifference of a machine. Ulysses felt like a pebble, sometimes carried to and fro, and sometimes abandoned, by the tide of unpity and misunderstanding. Sometimes the waves of the great current seized him, tossed him hither and thither all day unwittingly, and marooned him again at nightfall in the desert of some public square, whence the life, returning with daybreak, would take him and swirl him away once more in its irresistible flux. He, the master, had become the aimless vagabond once more. He dreamed with an empty stomach, his head humming with wonderful schemes. He was roused from his dreaming by the buffets of the swag-bellied, empty-pated multitude. In those crowded streets it seemed harder to find a helping hand than in the open spaces of the desert. The cannibals he had known seemed less hostile than these Americans who had come from every country of the white-skinned world. Only a few Negroes he met on the docks seemed to have human hearts hidden somewhere behind their bestial masks. The lynch law, a constant reminder that the tortures of their native lands only become more refined between white hands, keeps alive in their souls that element of sadness and brotherhood which can never be found in powerfully organized communities, and which subsists only among those whom they oppress. One Negro offered him a glass of beer in a saloon; another, a whole loaf of bread. That night, being less hungry than usual, Ulysses plucked up the courage to ask a fellow-countryman who owned a restaurant to give him a square meal, telling him at the same time that he could not pay for it till he had earned some money. He was even invited to spend the night at the home of his benefactor. A jug of resin-wine recalled his own country with strange poignancy. Antæus-like, this contact with his native land filled him with new strength, and when, ballasted by this food and wine, which, whatever their taste may be, have had the virtue of sharpening the spirit of a race through centuries of adversity, he trod the pavement again, it was with a firmer and more optimistic step.

But he went from defeat to defeat. With each new day, a higher wall seemed to stand between his hopes and their goal, while, little by little, hunger sapped his power of illusion. From the great city streets, he had passed to the mean back lanes of the slum quarters, and then to the docks, that last refuge of all that the human tide jostles and elbows toward the tide of the ocean, that they may take their leave, or drown.

One day, as he was lounging about the quays, with empty stomach and head, he caught sight of a Greek ship, the pennon of departure flapping on the mast. He went on board. Being at the end of all hope, he thought of repatriation. The second in command offered him a free crossing on the condition that he worked his passage, and let himself be disembarked at the first Greek port. Ulysses had a moment of weakness. He thought of returning to his island once more, where nobody died of hunger. But he hardened his heart when he thought of the scorn that is heaped on the head of the emigrant whose emigration has failed. The emigrant may die, but he must not give in. Too much ignominy awaits him on return if he has not succeeded. The *Americanos*—the Greek who has come back from America—must come back rich. Otherwise, he is dishonoured for ever. As soon as the anchor-chain began to creak, Ulysses ran down the gangway. In spite of everything, he preferred a plunge into the wretched life of the docks to the shame of returning, defeated, to Cephalonia.

New York, that great beast of prey, engulfed him anew, while the little parcel of his country moved off from the quay and vanished into the night. He stayed there for two hours following that shadow of happiness which was drifting away from him. Clenching his fists

[224]

and keeping his tears back, he saw the Greek flag salute American soil and disappear. Perhaps he would never see it again. Stevedores elbowed him, giant cranes threatened him with their enormous hooks. The noises of the port were deafening him, while his eyes were gazing at a sunlit island, as though in a dream.

A sharp impact summoned him from his reverie, as a porter jostled him. The crowd swallowed him again, and he began his interrupted and hopeless search once more.

At last he fell in with a certain Leonidas Papastrati-gopoulos, who sold Egyptian cigarettes in a modest way. Egyptian cigarettes have always been a Greek monopoly. The Turk did not know then how to handle the tobacco that his land produces, and Egypt never produced any. It needed the Greek to export Turkish tobacco, to make cunning blends of it and roll it in a certain way, before the triumph of the Egyptian cigarette was possible.

"What do you want of me?" asked Leonidas.

"Work, and a slice of bread," replied Ulysses, completing the gambit.

"Can you roll cigarettes?"

"No one has more than ten fingers, not even your best roller; I have got ten, too, and I'll roll as quickly and as well as another."

This answer pleased Leonidas. The Greek has a weakness for the novice. He thinks that he knows everything himself, and usually rubs shoulders with his equally omniscient fellows, so avowed ignorance flatters him, and predisposes him to goodwill.

"Let's try," said Leonidas. "From tomorrow onwards come here at seven every morning. I'll give you two cents for every twenty cigarettes."

In a week's time Ulysses was rolling eight hundred to a thousand cigarettes daily. He could go on rolling for fourteen hours running. When he is reduced to manual labour, the Greek is remarkable for his deft hands. The subtlety and rapidity of his brain being unemployed, it seems to escape through his fingers. As a waiter in a restaurant he handles plates, glasses, and cups with superhuman skill. As a tailor, he sews quicker and better than any other. In his hands, as a cobbler, the needle pierces and repierces the toughest leather with the speed and precision of a sewing machine. As carpenter, joiner, or wheelwright, he is truly λεπτουργός "maker of what is fine." Leonidas was not slow to appreciate the virtuosity of his new roller. He took Ulysses to live in his own house, so that he was able to put all his scanty wages on one side. In his spare moments, scarcely five minutes daily, he studied the secrets of mixing and blending tobacco. He learned the virtues of the golden, aromatic tobacco of Xanthe, and the properties of the *samsoun*, which serves principally as a saltpetre for quick lighting. Little by little he conceived schemes of his own, of possible blends that would better suit the American palate. A pinch of Virginia tobacco would be sure, he thought, to awaken a memory of their own soil that could not but be agreeable. In his restless mind he was already aiming at the immense custom of the New World, while Leonidas supplied only his own fellow-countrymen, a few thousand icecream-venders and flower-sellers, a few hundred restaurateurs and waiters.

When Ulysses became master of his trade, and of a sufficient number of dollars, he set out on his own account. Leonidas did not grudge him his going. Every Greek knows that the others want to buy and sell themselves, and that one stays at a fixed salary only while waiting to fly with one's own wings. The pinioned sandal of Hermes is more than a myth, it is the very stuff of the Hellenic soul.

Ulysses obtained, on credit, a small supply of every kind of tobacco. After several experiments, he managed to make a new cigarette, of a special flavour, whose composition he kept a secret. He peddled his products himself. He displayed his wares at the doors of theatres and large restaurants, Athenian fashion. An array of cigarettes hung from his neck and rested on his stomach, which had grown thin through over-work, late hours, and the handful of olives and the few onions that formed his miserable daily fare.

Such was the second beginning of Ulysses, former lord of the Sudan, collaborator of Kitchener, benefactor of the Holy Sepulchre and of his own country.

In rain, snow, cold, and heat, in contact with the

luxury he had known so well, and in the grip of poverty of which he had believed himself quit for ever, he made his rounds in the avenues, and stood for hours on propitious hunting grounds. No customer, no passer-by, could guess at the rise and fall of the man who offered these cigarettes. Nothing in his proud and self-confident bearing betrayed his inner discouragement, or tried to inspire pity.

Besides, Ulysses felt that his star was in the ascendant again. Every day he sold a few more cigarettes. At dawn he went home gaily, his step and soul unburdened of the weight of unsold cigarettes. In due course, he felt himself in a position to work with a companion, then with a second, and a third. He was becoming well known among the Greeks. When they talked of him, they said: "Ulysses? Eh, the κεραγά, the hornwearer! He is the son of a mother! The devil's sock! I tell you he was begotten in shame! He'll eat us all!"

These epithets among the Greeks are always a sure sign of predestined success.

But Ulysses was nearing forty. Now, more than ever before, he would have to act quickly. His little trade grew visibly, and he felt that he could soon lead it to security. But Ulysses had nothing of the bourgeois in him. Mediocrity, even superficially gilded, was not for him. His temperament, unloosed by the glory of his Sudanese success and in no wise dimmed by the Evil Hour that had followed, aspired to the greatest triumphs, the highest honours, to that mighty fortune

[228]

that hurls a man to the loftiest pinnacle, and holds him there.

Ulysses, under the influence of America, fell to meditating on advertisement. While he walked the streets and plied his trade, he watched the electric signs, those lighthouses of commerce, announcing, instead of rocks to avoid, lures to catch the passer-by, like latterday sirens. Ulysses distrusted them, perhaps through homonymic instinct. Besides, they seemed too hackneyed, and too expensive. Their influence is based on continuity, and Ulysses wanted an immediate effect. The sandwich-men who passed him in the street presented a monstrous outline which unconsciously outraged the feeling for pure line that lay deep-rooted in his Hellenic soul. The idea of advertisement in the daily papers pleased him more. The written word will always have an invincible attraction for the Greek. He consulted a publicity agent, and found that a single line would have ruined him in less than a week. He tried having the name of his brand shouted in the streets by professional criers. In spite of contrary advice, he refused to change his name, of which he was as proud as a French duke, or a prince of the Holy Roman Empire; but in American mouths it was so mangled and distorted that it lost all meaning, and sounded more like an incomprehensible blasphemy than a fruit-yielding hymn of praise.

"I must find something new, something beautiful . . ." he murmured to himself.

In the streets of New York, everything was ugly except the women, who were superb. These slim, well-knit, and athletic girls, with their exuberant beauty and well-being, began to attract his attention. This was the element to exploit, this nobility that dominated the grim surrounding drabness. One night, when he had been allowed to sell his cigarettes in one of the great night clubs, he saw a hundred beautiful chorus-girls dancing with a unity worthy of Kitchener's soldiers, each smoking a cigarette, and blowing the smoke through their lips in little rhythmic rings. This connexion of the American woman and the cigarette haunted him for several days. He saw that it could be exploited, but the background was lacking. A connecting link had to be found. These women could sell his cigarettes, and launch his brand for good. There were the women, and there were the cigarettes; the attic that served him as workroom, kitchen, dining-room, and bedroom was full of the latter. Outside, the throng of future clients passed on its way. He would have to take that throng by storm, put his "Ulysses" cigarettes into their mouths, through the agency of the chorus-girls.

The Greek being, above all, articulate, Ulysses began repeating to himself the object, the goal, and the means. "These women must put my cigarettes into the mouths of those men."

With his imagination full of the night-club scene, his room full of cigarettes, and his eyes full of the crowd that flowed beneath his windows, he repeated the formula a thousand times, like an equation to be solved.

"Eureka!" cried Ulysses all of a sudden. "I've found it."

"What have you found, Kyrie Ulysses?" asked one of his workmen. They believed he had gone mad.

"Insects!" replied Ulysses. "You have not got the brains of one small turkey-cock among you, and your skulls produce nothing but dung! Eureka! I've found it, I tell you! In a week I'll be rich, and you will all go on licking bones!"

These expressions, though insulting, represent a steadfast but triumphant friendship, and continued protection of the weak by the strong.

"We know that you could nail a horseshoe onto a house fly!" the workman answered. "But tell us your idea."

Ulysses' voice assumed the conference or newspaper-reading tone. With chosen words and long periods of Demosthenean syntax, embroiled by the inevitable emphasis of unfamiliar words, Ulysses recited, almost psalmodied, his prolix revelations. He unfolded his plan and painted its brilliant and immediate success in flaming colours.

"By God and the All-Holy!" his first workman cried when he had finished. "It is an idea from heaven!"

All that remained was to work out the expense. When they had reckoned out the necessary expenditure, they saw that Ulysses would not have a cent left.

In answer to a remark on their point, Ulysses hooked his thumbs into his waistcoat pockets, drumming his chest piano-wise with his fingers, and cried:

" 'We shall fight behind our shields or be brought home dead on our shields!' as our ancestors said at Sparta! Victory or death! If it works, I shall be rich, and I shall make you all rich too. If it fails, I shall leave this accursed town, and may God be with you!"

As has been already seen, the plan succeeded beyond all hopes. The very next day, he had to take twenty fresh workmen into his service. For months the only work he did was to examine the ever-increasing figures in his books. His different branches, with their richly garnished windows, all exactly the same, were proudly established in the wealthiest avenues. His workrooms already filled a large building. He sent for specialists from Cavalla and Cairo. The debts that he had left in Egypt were all paid, and his account at the bank was gorged with dollars. He paid only by cheque now, and was beginning to find that even in America the cigarette market had its limits. When questioned about his success, Ulysses would answer modestly:

"What can I say, my children? To drag myself out of the misery into which I had fallen, the tobacco trade had its points; but it does not satisfy a man. After all, what is it but smoke?"

The day was not slow in coming when the smoke became flesh. A great syndicate was founded. One of the greatest New York financiers had asked him to call. He was led into a large office where several directors were already assembled.

"How much will you take," they asked him, "for your whole concern? How much down, and how many of our shares?"

Ulysses who had been studying this side of the question for some time, asked seven hundred and fifty thousand dollars in cash, and the same in shares.

The bargain was soon struck. They insisted on the condition that he should have no concern in the manufacture and sale of cigarettes for twenty years. He sacrificed the trade of which he had tired, with difficulty, judging that the relinquishing of it ought to bring him in several more thousand dollars. He got them after a few minutes' bargaining.

Ulysses was rich again.

Having remade his fortune, he retired to Florida to rest. He thought of returning to Greece, but could not make up his mind.

He had learned to distrust the honours that are heaped upon the newly rich; and he feared the deep patriotism that still subsisted in his heart. He did not feel himself strong enough to face his own people yet. But, his only commercial activity being to draw on his bank for his own modest needs, and those of his parents and relations (to whom he had resumed his former monthly remittances), Ulysses was bored to death.

Idleness, even gilded idleness, held no charms for him. The black broth of the Lacedæmonians was a hundred times more fitting than the delights of Capua.

Floating in a clear sky of wealth and leisure, he watched the horizon with the gaze of an eagle, whose instinct it is, even after satiety, to swoop down upon any new prey.

A black speck fixed his attention.

18

⸎⸎⸎

NINETEEN HUNDRED AND FIVE; Agadir! A thunderclap in a clear sky. Liége, Antwerp, Mons, Verdun, the Marne, and the Somme make these three syllables, with which the whole world echoed for months, and which haunted the imagination of Europe until 1914, seem pale and insignificant. The ranting of mountebanks on the stage of a little African village, which ended in a true drama; the age-old lath and slapstick of Harlequinade, that one night puddled the planking with human blood; the death of millions of men, the anguish of humanity, and the drawn-out course of a war that has disintegrated several empires and all consciences present a picture of such magnitude that it is hard to link it with such a clownish origin.

When, from his aerie, Ulysses espied the threatening storm and saw that Europe was gathering at Algeciras in an effort to stay the tempest, he realized that peace was hanging by a narrow thread.

Son of the only race that has lived through the ages of bronze, gold, and iron in the full and uninterrupted consciousness of its own national entity, he realized that the steel age was at hand.

Ten years with the Mahdi, the daily necessity of assuring his head on its shoulders, and of reading the true meaning in the most secret and twisted thoughts, had developed his political sense. The Book of Life, wherein the logic of events and their future courses reveals its ineluctable laws, was the only one over which he had ever pored; but he knew it by heart, and he had a wonderfully clear vision of the immediate future. He saw Europe arming, and he knew that mankind is ever impatient to wield the arms that it has sharpened. The more the chancelleries talked of peace, the more certain he became that war would follow war. In Greece, when insults are hurled and returned, there is no danger; but when two men who have quarrelled greet each other politely and exchange obsequious salutes, the knife is always at hand to settle their differences.

Ulysses resolved to make armament his new profession. Having grown rich through tobacco smoke, he determined to enrich himself further through the smoke of gunpowder. He had emerged with profit from the steel of the Mahdi's lances; now, rich and strong in his long and painfully acquired experience, he knew that he would prosper amidst the steel of the white men's cannons.

[236]

But he had to take the road once more, and, as the Greek phrase goes, "run his work." For Ulysses, as for many of his compatriots, sedentary work was incomprehensible. Throughout Greece, movement seems the very key to profit. It is the Mercurian complex, the instinct of the intermediary who flies from seller to buyer.

In the trade that he had just abandoned, only the actual peddling had been in harmony with his nature. As soon as success had not only relieved him of the task, but made it impossible, his work had lost all interest, and in spite of his ever-mounting profits, the blight of immobility weighed heavily upon him.

The Greeks have invented a profession that is unknown to most other races; a man can be said to be an "air-merchant." This profession consists of selling something that one has not actually got, but which is wanted by someone else who does not know where to find it. An air-merchant scents a transaction at once, no matter what the merchandise or "object" of exchange may be—a stock of groceries, a house, a horse, or a bundle of shares. Of him it is also said that he "does business on his feet," having no office or fixed headquarters. He haunts the quays, the commercial thoroughfares, the halls of important banks, and even drawing-rooms; wherever there is talk of business, he is there. His ever-watchful curiosity strikes contact with the needs and appetites that brush him in passing. He catches scents, observes spoors, follows trails. The

[237]

profession is full of failures, refusals and humiliations, sleepless nights and breadless days. But when the business succeeds, after one has been the connecting link between the offer and the demand for commodities that one has never possessed, and which one has, perhaps, not even seen, the material and moral satisfaction is so great that it compensates for all previous reverses.

Transposed to a higher plane, the air-merchant is also called a great financier, he is the man who handles the money, the goods, and the reputations of others.

Ulysses, like all Greeks, had the air-trading spirit in his blood. He was about to exploit it in a way that would astonish the world. But the first condition was to assure his position in the heart of Big Business. London attracted him as much as Paris; there, he knew, was the axis around which the greatest commercial activities revolved, and he determined to go there, and he, who had landed at New York as a steerage passenger on the deck, booked a luxury suite on the most modern and magnificent transatlantic liner. He installed himself as if he had spent his whole life in such surroundings, crossing and recrossing the "Big Pond." He wisely decided to take a valet with him, to make an impression in the eyes of the other travellers; and to justify the presence of his valet, he had to enlarge his wardrobe.

While he was arranging Ulysses' trunk and suitcases, the steward wondered if their owner was an English peer or a partner in Morgan's New York bank. When he appeared on deck, he was taken for the most distinguished passenger. The *maître d'hotel*, who knew nothing about him, gave him the best table in the immense dining-room. When he passed the conductor of the orchestra on the way to his place, the musician bent low before him, which is the supreme homage in great restaurants.

But Ulysses was not travelling to be showered with honours. He was working towards an entirely different goal. This voyage was his apprenticeship in really big business. He had to keep his eyes open. At a near-by table he noticed a little old man who was shabbily dressed, but encircled by a mysterious halo of importance. The restaurant staff paid no particular attention to him but, judging only by the way he sat down in his chair, one felt he was a person squarely seated in his personality, sure of himself and sure of the morrow.

Other passengers looked more important. They travelled with numerous staffs. One could hear the rattle of typewriters in their state-rooms. Secretaries swarmed about them. To Ulysses all this agitation seemed the sign of men who were eager to arrive, being still in the ascent. Only the little old man gave him the impression of the goal, of realization, of the man whose only task is to keep the situation which is his. He might be a useful acquaintance to make. Ulysses would have to get to know him, without haste and without seeming eager. Above all, he would have to pose as a personage himself, by establishing defensive isolation.

Ulysses realized that, in his new undertaking, he could no longer play the quick-witted little Greek who takes fortune by storm. To hold his own in international affairs, where the threads were in the hands of all the great figures of world politics, he would have to raise himself to an infinitely superior level.

The atmosphere in which he now wanted to forge his way was no longer that of small, or even of great, commerce; it was an atmosphere heavy with intrigues, speeches, declarations, *notes verbales*, and diplomatic interviews; an atmosphere poisoned with attitudes and insincerity; an atmosphere that can be breathed only by the chosen few, whose lungs are powerful enough. But Ulysses was quick in acclimatizing himself. Aboard this great liner that was carrying from one shore of the Atlantic to the other all the appetites of the Anglo-Saxon world, on which war and peace depended, he became a different man. He surrounded himself with silence. He assumed the attitude of the man who knows and waits, strong in the knowledge that the world cannot do without him. He asked for the list of passengers. There he found the name of A. I. Schmidt, President of the Nazareth Steel and Armament Company. It was just the man he needed. Was it the little old man? It was. That German name, tinged with dissimulated Judaism, did not displease Ulysses. It would make the contact easier. The pure Anglo-Saxon is difficult to handle at the first encounter. For the success of his plan, he had to effect a carefully worked out, stealthy approach.

One evening, as he walked round the deck, he arranged that his path should cross that of the important person. At the third crossing, Ulysses, well versed in Anglo-Saxon ways, said:

"Fine weather, sir."

"Yes, sir," answered the old American, "very fine weather." And both of them walked on in opposite directions.

Later on they met in the smoking-room. The old American, at his fifth whisky and soda, was ripe for confidences, and Ulysses, at his second coffee and fourth glass of water, was ready to receive them. Ulysses was not slow in confessing that he was one of the company's shareholders. He asked a few guarded questions. But he carefully avoided any indiscreet questioning, which puts all Anglo-Saxons, even if they are German Jews, on their guard, and makes them dub their questioners "a damn sight too pushing." Ulysses maintained a modest but vigilant reserve.

He soon learned that the armament firm was owed a considerable sum by Venezuela for a supply of cannons, and that all attempts at collecting it had failed, in spite of the energetic intervention of the United States Government. Ulysses extracted all the details of the affair. Knowing the mentality of debtors, by experience, he immediately understood the whole situation better than the creditors. But, deeming it premature to offer his services, he remarked only that he was going to Venezuela himself about a deal in sugar.

In the morning, uncertain as to what he had said the day before in his haze of whisky fumes, the American asked Ulysses if he had really said he was going to Venezuela too. Ulysses repeated his intention, and when the American suggested that he could perhaps be of some service there, Ulysses replied with the modesty of an Englishman:

"I can hardly believe that I could be of any use where your powerful company and even your Government have gone astray."

The old American liked this answer.

"Who knows?" he said. "Our great organizations, and especially our State Department, are too heavy-handed for a certain type of business. With these South Americans one must have a free hand and plenty of suppleness. You are Greek, I think?"

Ulysses did not hide the fact, and the American went on:

"You southern races can understand one another."

Anglo-Saxon geography is a surprising thing. It divides the globe into whites and browns. The whites are the Anglo-Saxons and Scandinavians; they are northern, even if they come from Australia. The browns are southern, even if they skirt the North Sea. Lord Chesterfield said: "The Orient begins at Calais," and, according to this system, the Occident is not of the south unless it is really southern, while the whole Orient is of the south, even the ice-bound reaches of northernmost Japan.

Ulysses had carried his modesty far enough. He feared that, if he went too far, he would lose a good opportunity. So he offered his services, and they were accepted. And when the old American declared that business was business, Ulysses had the courage to refuse any preliminary agreement. When the other insisted, he declared with astonishing magnanimity:

"Listen, sir; I have to go to Venezuela anyway. I should be delighted to be of any service to you. But I still know nothing of the situation there or of what lines to work on. Once I am there, I will keep you abreast of everything I do. A company like yours will never let me down."

As far as remuneration went, Ulysses relied more on his own resources than on the most favourable of preliminary contracts.

During the last days of his voyage, Ulysses and the old American were inseparable. It was definitely agreed that Ulysses should go to Venezuela as soon as possible. The great financier's two secretaries tried in vain to make him accept a cheque to cover his travelling expenses. Ulysses appeared almost offended and refused to accept anything except a letter introducing him to the Venezuelan War Minister. To travel at his own expense, and not to fix any remuneration in advance, seemed to him the best way to turn it to better account if he made a great success of the mission. Besides, he had no doubt of it. Ulysses was not one of those mediocre spirits for whom a modest security has an insurmountable charm. He was of the same stuff as all great adventurers, who seize hold of fortune to such purpose that it cannot but help them.

At Caracas he felt at his ease immediately; everything there was disorderly and arbitrary, for a dictator made and unmade the laws at the promptings of his fancy. Having mastered the Mahdi, "the Lion of the Nile," President Castro, "the Ape of the Andes," was not the type to intimidate Ulysses. Besides, he liked the country from his first moments of contact with it. Several Greeks had made their fortunes there and occupied enviable situations in the capital. He was recognized by them the moment he arrived and invited to join in their Greek fare. The savoury smell of pilaff, the stuffed tomatoes, the oil, and the honey cakes set his subtle wits in readiness. He soon learned that the elegant Christo, the best hairdresser in Caracas, waved the hair of Eleonore, the dictator's mistress, and that Doña Teresa, his lawful wife, entrusted hers to Yorghi, the other Greek hairdresser. As these two women dared not come to blows openly, for fear of the dictator, they avenged themselves by patronizing different hairdressers, and the hairdressers, being Greeks, avenged themselves by seizing the presidency of the Greek community of Caracas by turns. At the elections, each menaced the other with the thunderbolts of his client. The Greek colony, being divided between these two rivals, generally opted for the barber of the lawful wife. To have voted for the other would have seemed slightly dishonourable, smacking faintly of the shame of the pimp's calling. For the Greek will ply any trade save that of the ρουφιάνο, the ruffian, the harlot's bully. In all its forms, even the most indirect, even if only by voting for the lawful wife's barber, rather than for the mistress's barber, marital honour is, for the Greeks, a fetish with which there can be no compromise. Nevertheless, for their personal affairs, some members of the Greek colony at Caracas, mostly the young bloods and the bachelors, never the married men, had a tendency, which they dared not openly declare, to patronize Christo, judging him more useful than the hairdresser of Doña Teresa. Ulysses was with them from the start.

When he demanded an audience, all the officials of the President's civil and military households refused it in turn. Christo obtained it for him immediately.

The first interview with "the Ape of the Andes" was a stormy one. As soon as Ulysses had revealed the object of his mission, the President lost his temper and charged that the shells with which he had been supplied did not go off. The cannons were, according to him and his numerous generals, of bad quality. No engagement had been kept by his creditors; he was determined not to pay; he had said it again and again to the United States Minister.

Ulysses let the storm blow over, and replied:

"Illustrious Señor Presidente! As I speak bad French and have not the honour to speak Spanish, you have not understood me. I have not come to take money. I am acquainted with the state of the Venezuelan budget. Your deficits have been mounting for the last five years. I should be quite mad if I thought that you would pay for shells that do not explode, and cannons that always do."

The Ape of the Andes thought he was dreaming. Never had a representative of any of his numerous creditors spoken to him in such a strain. He noticed that he had forgotten to ask Ulysses to sit down.

"Señor Ulysses," he said, "pray be seated. You astonish me. What do you propose, then? More cannons on credit?"

"Please God, not!" replied Ulysses. "The quality is far too bad."

"I understand nothing of all this," said the President laughing.

"Nor I, Señor Presidente," said Ulysses. "You have been quarrelling with my firm for five years; your quarrel is now in the hands of our two Governments. Your relations with the United States have become envenomed. My company is powerful in a country where financial power can elect or depose the President; it is not like here, where merit alone leads to honours. So why draw unpleasantness on yourself over a trifle?"

"A trifle?" interrupted Castro. "Nine million dollars

plus interest at six percent for five years a trifle?"

"If the payment of these nine million dollars can bring in ten or twelve, am I not right to say that it is only a trifle?"

"Señor!" exclaimed Castro. "Allow me, with all due deference, to tell you that you are quite mad. . . ."

"Señor Presidente," said Ulysses, "with all due deference, may it be permitted of a humble traveller to say that you are a great general and a great orator, but that in financial matters you are just as childish as the president of my company and the United States Secretary of the Treasury?"

"Caramba, Señor Ulysses! I shall summon my own Finance Minister, who is a descendant of those Jews that were converted by the Holy Inquisition, and who understand figures better than all the Greeks since the time of your glorious ancestor and namesake."

"Above all, do not do that," replied Ulysses. "What I have to tell you is strictly confidential. Only we two must know about it and profit by it. The slightest indiscretion would spoil everything, and my scheme is so simple, a child could understand it. Can you dispose of a million dollars in three months?"

"I can dispose of much more . . . if I choose, I can dispose of all Venezuela, all the cash-boxes, all the banks, all the territory, and anyone that annoys me," said the dictator proudly, "and of any foreigner that comes and meddles with my affairs."

"That's perfect. The agreement is certain!" con-

[247]

cluded Ulysses. "Now I ask only for five minutes' patience and all your attention.

"My company has a capital of twenty-five million dollars divided into two hundred and fifty thousand shares of one hundred dollars each. For five years it has been paying no dividends, because you owe it nine million dollars. The hundred-dollar shares have fallen to fifty. If you pay, the shares will immediately shoot up to two or three hundred. Buying fifty thousand shares at fifty would be enough to gain all the money that you have to pay, with a million dollars left over. I shall find credit for you in London banks of seventy-five percent of it against the security of the shares that you buy. So you need only six hundred and twenty-five thousand dollars to pay your debt and make a million dollars! Who understands business better, your Jew, or the little Greek who has the honour to present his homage?"

Castro had risen. Ulysses rose and heard the following little speech:

"Illustrious offspring of that race which I have always admired since my tenderest youth, when, at my desk at school, I learned the fables of Æsop, come that I may kiss you!"

So Ulysses received the presidential accolade. Castro begged him to put down his plan on paper, with all the figures. With his nimble fingers Castro checked the whole scheme. Finding everything accurate and clear, he cried:

[248]

"By St. James of Compostela! It is all just as you say; but I think I can improve on it. It is only right that my country should pay a part of its debt, were it only two or three million dollars. . . ."

Ulysses then admitted that this administrative honesty was the crowning success of his project. He could not see why the personal good of the President should not proceed from a sum that Venezuela would be called upon to provide. Knowing the hearts of men through long experience, he was not at all surprised by this sudden change in the President.

That evening, after the momentous interview, Ulysses went to the theatre and sat in the President's box. By an odd coincidence, that night, a French company performed *Les affaires sont les affaires* by Octave Mirbeau.

Ulysses stayed another month in Caracas, which was the time needed to get in touch with the bankers of the Venezuelan Government in London. He had to prevent all contact between Venezuela and the New York market. Every day, Castro received a telegram announcing the purchase of a bundle of shares of which Ulysses had his allotment. These purchases made the stock rise slightly, but the operation was concluded at a very reasonable figure. When Castro and Ulysses had bought all they needed, a presidential *communiqué* announced the settlement of the debt by scaled payments. The company shares went up with a bound. All Wall Street wanted to buy them. Ulysses' prophecies were left far behind, and the debt was liquidated with a profit of more than three hundred dollars per share.

In this way Castro came into favour again with the White House, and no one ever knew that the Venezuelan debt to the United States had been paid by the United States itself, buying at four hundred what it had just sold for less than a hundred.

During this period, Ulysses was covered with honours. Castro invited him to stay in the presidential palace. The representatives of all the powers gave large dinners for him, one after the other. The United States Minister was authorized to express his Government's gratitude in an official address, and by letter. A great New York paper wrote a long article about him, calling him "the mystery man," a title which was never to leave him. President Castro offered him the portfolio of Finance, which Ulysses modestly declined. He wanted to leave as soon as possible the country where his success had been too great. The President, who knew to the last cent what Ulysses had made on the deal, might at any moment find the sum exaggerated; and, on the other hand, Ulysses knew too much about the whole affair. So he thought it only prudent to put the whole ocean, at least, between his powerful partner and himself.

The atmosphere of Caracas had often proved unhealthy to Castro's friends. Ulysses felt that he was carefully watched, and the President's immediate associates were certainly not friendly towards him. Ulysses confided his apprehension to the United States Minister, who promised him his protection, because of the great service he had rendered to the interests of his country.

Finally, after duly taking his leave of the President, Ulysses embarked on an American warship. In this way he returned to New York, having left Egypt a few years before as a deck passenger on a little Greek steamer. On arrival, he was invited to attend a full board meeting, especially summoned, to receive the thanks of the company, and a cheque for a considerable sum of money. The chairman of the board of directors made a little speech, in which he praised Ulysses and his forefathers of the time of Pericles, citing Homer and Alexander the Great. Few of his illustrious ancestors were forgotten. Ulysses replied, citing George Washington and Benjamin Franklin. Since his elevation, Ulysses had acquired a certain culture and could make a pretty speech, which was sweetened, rather than exaggerated, by his Greek sonority.

After the meeting, the chairman ushered him into his office, and proposed that he should represent the company for all foreign orders, with a seat on the board, and a percentage on all the business transacted in his department. Ulysses had a sudden flash of genius:

"My dear President," he said, "I thank you, but I cannot yet accept your proposition. You do not know me. I have just done you a great service, but you know

[251]

nothing of the details of the affair, nor of my past life. Before you entrust your interests to me officially, you must know who I am, and all about my stormy life."

The Greek feels a great need to excuse himself. Proud of his race, of the purity of its living and of the acuteness of its wits, he feels himself, come what may, burdened with original sin for which he must atone; not for sins of commission, but of omission; the omission of all the heroism, all the excellence, all the perfection attributed to his forefathers. Homer, Herodotus, Plato, Socrates, Praxiteles, Aristotle, Demosthenes, Alexander the Great, the Venus de Milo, and the Apollo Belvedere, these are the deep-rooted flaw of the Greek. He has dragged this ball-and-chain clanking behind him through the Empire of Byzantium for more than a thousand years, through five hundred years of slavery, and through more than a century of reconquered freedom. He trails too many great names behind him. He cannot enjoy the esteem of which he would be worthy did these crushing comparisons not exist. And here the Greek is himself at fault, not so much through his actual inferiority as through the past superiority which he exaggerates. Creator of gods and legends, the spirit of Greece was so exalted that it could not maintain its self-imposed mission and lofty attitude through so many æons of history. The poets, the historians, and the philosophers, in their need to make gods to themselves, exalted their chosen to such a height that they made them the models of eternity.

Today a whole breed of men is condemned by these models, and suffers from them. A gallery of marbles brings a long succession of generations to judgment, all living, generous, daring, and brave, but, as all living-kind, imperfect. The myth of Leonidas, about which the Persian chroniclers are strangely silent, indicts the Greek of cowardice by comparison; and the statues of Apollo, of unbeauty, and Aristides, of dishonesty; and this last shame is stressed by an eclipse of five long centuries. All nations have flowered and borne fruit in the noonday sun of history. For five centuries, the Greek disappeared and, when he emerged again, he seemed other than the image that men had fashioned of his ancestors. He seemed too small. The Greek wishes, and has succeeded in his wish, to be called to judgment for the manifold perfections that have sprung from his imagination alone, that imagination which has engendered so much unearthly beauty.

May he endure the travails of the Godhead into which he fashioned himself, though he merit *"ni cet excès d'honneur, ni cette indignité!"*

So Ulysses made a complete and sincere confession, hiding nothing. More, to intensify the merit of his sincerity, he invented indelicacies that he had never committed. He well knew that the envious, carping at his success, would blacken his name with calumny, and profit by his Greek birth and his numerous reverses, to make him out a dangerous adventurer. His speculations on the company's shares might at any moment transpire from Caracas or London. He preferred to take the bull by the horns, to bring all malevolence to nothing beforehand, by speaking more ill of himself than anyone could possibly invent.

This confession had the desired effect. The President said that the frankness of his attitude made him a still more invaluable collaborator.

So Ulysses was launched into big business and high finance as the accredited representative of the greatest armament firm in the world.

They decided that he should make Paris his general headquarters. Like all Greeks, he had a special veneration for Paris, without ever having been there. There, he felt, was the hub of the modern world, the great meeting place where wits were keenest, where all currents crossed.

19

✿✿

IN Paris Ulysses established himself magnificently. He rented an old *hôtel* in the Rue Malesherbes. Louis XV was then in high fashion, so he sat in *bergères* that had once enshrined the panniered and powdered marquises of the eighteenth century, and did his accounts and all his subtle reckonings at a writing-table signed by Riesener, with bronzes by Gouthière. His door was opened by a footman six feet tall, his table was served by a venerable butler whose sidewhiskers had whitened in the service of three dukes. The manner and bearing of his new master never jarred on him. Only the dishes that it was sometimes his lot to tender shocked his nostrils. By the side of a chef who had been recommended by Paillard there was a Greek cook who concocted such dishes as vine leaves stuffed with rice and raisins, which seemed indecent and vulgar to the Frenchman.

Learning that any financier worthy of the name must have at least two secretaries, Ulysses generously equipped himself with a French marquis—the Marquis de Lène—and an English baronet—Sir Arthur New-fold. For his real work, he took a young compatriot, a doctor-at-law of the University of Paris and professor of everything that was to be known in the Place of the Constitution in Athens. This square—the Syntagma—is full of similar Pico della Mirandolas, who know everything that can be divined by a nimble mind, and affirm it with all the authority of a French or German degree. Strong in the Sorbonne or Heidelberg, they astonish their fathers and mothers with the most subversive proposals, and refuse to take their place in the Hellenic order of things until a substantial dowry can gild their fading laurels.

Ulysses saw no one; a little through native modesty, and largely through future pride. A judicious reserve exalts the one who can maintain it. He avoided, above all others, his compatriots. If no one is a prophet in his own country, he is still less so among his own people in another. Arrivists who leave their country exercise a great professional severity. Those who have succeeded are eager to keep their great privilege intact, and those who have failed detest their cleverer or more fortunate competitors. Greek communities established in the great capitals of Europe are divided into a few chosen ones, who, having managed to make a situation for themselves in society, are savagely jealous of their aristocratic frequentations, or what they believe are such, and all the others avenge their own modest station by blackening the names of the chosen, and of the illustrious natives with whom they mix. These two camps either know nothing of, or malign, each other, and meet only at church, where the haughtiness of the one and the bitterness of the other are moderated by the droning of the pope and the narcotic effect of the incense. The differences are levelled for a moment by the same gestures, the same signs of the cross, and the tapers lighted at the same candlestick, where, for a short moment, the fingers of the great banker and the humble waiter touch. Then the one goes his way to pay his court to some Philhellenic or needy duchess, the other to put his napkin over his arm once more. Abroad, social differences are not adjusted by origin but more by destination and cause, which is the more or less money gained, and mostly by the effect, which is the drawing-rooms where one is received. So that a former grocer's boy may, from the heights of the Faubourg St.-Germain or Mayfair, look down upon a direct descendant of the Phanariot princes or the heroes of the War of Greek Independence, who frequents only the Café de la Paix or Simpson's in the City. And this social climbing is so strong that it prevails even over money. In the land of immigration the richest is not necessarily the most envied. He often takes a lower place than someone less rich but who moves in higher circles. The pursuit of wealth gives way before the pursuit of social standing, which is still more chancy, being the realm of women. In their hands the struggle

[257]

is embittered by competition in clothes, by Chanel against Lanvin, and by youth and beauty, as much as by the husband's situation.

As soon as he arrived in Paris, Ulysses saw at a glance that the struggle had no place for him. He had no wife to draw him into it, and the power he had acquired freed him from all contact, on the condition that he withdrew himself like a hermit. Society is a dangerous system of cog-wheels; as soon as one touches it, the whole body is involved. Ulysses was not without snobbery, but his was of a superior kind. He could not see himself at the feet of dowagers; he saw them, on the contrary, running after him. This being instinctively his social attitude, isolation served his turn better than grovelling and reverence. His two secretaries, the Frenchman and the Englishman, were not slow to tempt him. They offered to open all the doors that were already ajar and others that were less easily forced. He refused their invitations with a proud consistency that impressed them profoundly. His young Greek secretary suggested some visits to the notabilities of the Greek colony. "Go towards the good!" Ulysses answered. "They have got nothing to sell me, and they have not got enough money to buy anything that I have to sell."

Gradually, the invisible man began to disturb his compatriots. He ordered his secretaries to give generous succour to the needy; to all the rest who welled about him like a flood, he closed his door without ceremony. Neither one nor the other ever saw him. So much so that, when he went to the Greek church for the interminable ceremonies of Eastertide, which no Greek, however free-thinking or atheist he may be, can avoid, it was an event. The pope, to whom the deacon had whispered, between the responses, of Ulysses' presence, almost lost the thread of his prayer, and covered his confusion only by a fit of one of those coughs which are the salvation of all embarrassed orators who have gone astray.

When Ulysses, dropping his generous offering through the slot of the alms-box, chose the most modest taper in the rack, all those who were sitting on the neighbouring bench offered him lights from the candles in their hands. Ulysses' candle had the honour of being kindled at six flames simultaneously, all ajog with the emotion of the hands that held them. He bore it with a firm and distant step to the icon of the All-Holy, which he kissed devoutly; then he retired to the obscurest stall, under the dazzled eyes of the congregation. His name flew round the church in a hissing undertone. The choir sang falser than usual in its emotion; the deacon, with his fine voice, forced his chanting to such a pitch that he risked a break for the first time in his life; and the priest, by an inconceivable error, censed the left side first, instead of the right, so great was his haste to bear his thurible to the corner where Ulysses lay hid. One of the archons even went so far as to offer him the seat of honour. Gently nodding his great head with its over-long hair and its already white moustache, Ulysses refused with the cold politeness of the very great. He left so discreetly before the end of the service that only his immediate neighbours noticed his departure. When the Mass was finished, in that intimate throng in the church porch where it is so easy to scrape acquaintance in the bustle, everyone was bitterly disappointed. Their mysterious compatriot had robbed them of an excellent opportunity of getting to know him. It was lost for a whole year. Gossip flourished like a weed. Some said he was the intimate friend of all the crowned heads; others, more embittered, declared that he was a fugitive from justice, dreading recognition by his fellow-countrymen; and others, especially the young women, attributed his bearing to the ascetic melancholy of a great and unhappy love. In this cloud of malice, calumny, and romantic imagination, the only definite fact that left its trail behind him was the prestige of the unknowable.

Ulysses played the part with consummate skill. He had been only a few months in Paris when his name ran freely in every circle of high finance and the parliamentary lobbies. Every deal in armaments was attributed to him. He was at the bottom of a thousand schemes of which he had never heard. Like calumny, praise is a light breeze, scarcely a breath at first, that grows from mouth to mouth into a tempest. At first whispered close to the ear, fable is added to fable, till, one day, it bursts into a clap of thunder.

For Ulysses, the thunderclap was the Turkish affair. Turkey was about to place an enormous order for big guns, shells, and rifles. Every armament firm was ablaze with eagerness. Boards of directors prepared their offers. A hubbub of commercial travellers filled the Pera Palace and Tokatlyan's in Constantinople. The largest military order that any state had ever made was in the balance.

Ulysses was the last to leave home. His firm had begun to grow impatient, and every day he received long cables. He was in touch with all the latest information. They hastened him to start and not to leave the field open to competitors too long. He answered, reassuring them in laconic cablegrams, but still did not leave Paris. For the moment he judged that his presence there was particularly useful.

Montmartre has always been the favourite meeting place of illustrious orientals. Through them, he was able to establish useful connexions and to land in Turkey armed with letters of introduction that would, in one day, destroy the months' old work of his competitors. On the banks of the Golden Horn these links would be more difficult and more compromising. He had given his two secretaries unlimited credit for their nights at the Moulin Rouge, the Rat Mort, and other haunts where the descendants of Mohammed nightly diluted in champagne the blood of their murders on the Bosporus. Every morning Sir Arthur Newfold and the Marquis de Lène made a report of their successes of the previous night. Champagne augurs well for confidence, and Ulysses began to see clearly into the secrets of Yildiz. The quarrels of the imperial family, the underside of politics, the mysteries of nomination and disgrace, let slip from lips heavy with wine—everything fell into place in his brain, and helped him to form his plan. A magnificent ex-Grand Vizier, scattering gold to right and left in the effort to discard his unconquerable boredom, and in debt to all the merchants in the Rue de la Paix and to all the restaurants, was brought to him by Sir Arthur.

Ulysses received him with the respectful politeness of a simple business man towards the mighty of this world, but also with the condescension of the successful man towards one who can just about keep his head above water.

When Hamid Pasha began to explain his circumstances, Ulysses interrupted him with a gesture of Mazarin protecting the young majesty of Louis XIV, or of Lord Beaconsfield covering the first escapades of the Prince of Wales with his authority.

"Your Highness," he said, "it does not become you to persuade me. I cannot venture to elicit explanations from Your Highness. I can only accept commands. And in this case the command is the figure."

Hamid Pasha quoted it. It was a large sum. Ulysses doubled it with the words:

"You, the great of the world, must be very bad accountants; and the contrary would be a sin of lese-majesty. Exact calculation should be left to us. You must certainly be in need of much more than you can now remember."

When the Pasha thanked him, and began to talk of repayment, Ulysses interrupted him:

"I would be a poor financier indeed, if I could not find a way of making this sum for you. At the right moment, you shall have an interest in my next important deal, which will, I hope, leave you a clear profit when I have been paid back. As the company of a solitary old man like me cannot hold many charms for you, my secretary, Sir Arthur, will keep you in touch with the affair."

A few days later Ulysses received the most cordial letters of introduction to the Grand Vizier and the Master of the Ordnance.

He arrived at Constantinople accompanied by the Marquis de Lène, who brought a whole library of dazzlingly bound catalogues, in which the factories, the machines, and their products were represented by photographs, of which each one was a masterpiece of idealized reproduction. But in one of his suitcases Ulysses had two catalogues quite unlike the rest, bound in Morocco leather of the finest Spanish craftsmanship.

He took up his quarters in a palace on the Asiatic shore of the Bosporus, put at his disposal by Hamid Pasha. He remained unnoticed, as he had wished. Dispatching his letters of introduction in the hands of the Marquis de Lène, he was received by the Grand Vizier the very next day in his villa at Bebek. Fearing the indiscretions of all government offices, and the poisonous atmosphere of red tape, Ulysses had asked, through Hamid Pasha, for a more intimate interview, and had obtained it. A minister who receives you in his own house, unencumbered by his office boys, secretaries, and departmental chiefs, is already more human. In the intimacy of his hearth, in the neighbourhood of his wife and children, whose cheerful shouts sometimes interrupt the business in hand, he loses something of his statesman's reasoning, and acquires something of the simpler reasoning of domesticity.

Ulysses went to his audience alone, taking one of his special catalogues with him. In spite of his recommendations, he was received with the customary formality of statesmen; a stiffness that is relaxed only before the sovereign in autocratic countries, and before the electorate in democratic ones.

The Grand Vizier received him standing, as for an interview that is intended to be a short one. Ulysses sat down. The Minister had either to have him shown to the door, or sit down himself. He preferred to sit down.

"Your Excellency," said Ulysses, "I represent the greatest armament house in the United States. I do not ask for any special favour. I rely entirely on the excellence of my products."

"You are acquainted with our needs," replied the

Minister. "What are your conditions? We already have plenty of proposals from your principal competitors. It is needless to say that, for an order on which the defence of the country depends, I cannot be satisfied on the strength of the introductions presented by your secretary, from whatever high quarter they may come. I shall choose the firm that offers me the best conditions. Submit your proposals in writing. They will be judged with the most severe impartiality."

"Your Excellency, I am pressed for time and can only stay for two days in Constantinople. Here is my complete catalogue. I will leave it with you. You will find all the necessary information in its pages. May I ask you to study it before any further discussion? May I also ask you to receive me again tomorrow, to hear your opinion?"

Ulysses had already stood up and taken leave of the Vizier, putting the voluminous catalogue, solidly packed, bound, and sealed, into his hands.

The next day Ulysses was received at the appointed time. His reception was as cold as it had been the night before. Ulysses could be certain only that his catalogue was nowhere to be seen on the Grand Vizier's writing-table.

"Sir," said the latter, combing his long beard with his fingers, "I have personally studied your catalogue. It is absorbing. I found information there that interested me profoundly, but it seemed incomplete. Is there no second volume?"

[265]

"Your Excellency," replied Ulysses, "your perspicacity is truly astonishing. I am unpardonably careless. I thought I had given you both the published volumes of the catalogue. The second is in my briefcase. Here it is."

He handed the second volume to the Minister and added:

"There are two more in press. They will only be ready in a few days, and I will give them to you as soon as they appear. They will be useful for settling the details of the order, if your Government should decide to entrust it to me."

The ice was broken. Ulysses' catalogues each contained, on each of its two hundred and fifty quarto pages, not banal and deceptive photographs, but two authentic ten-pound notes, clean and new, prettily bound in *passe-partout*, whence it was easy to extract them without crumpling or tearing. Armed with two catalogues, the Minister had already ten thousand pounds; when the contract was signed, he could count on two more volumes. The house that Ulysses represented really deserved to get the contract. It got it.

The final negotiations lasted a few days more, but things went quickly enough. There were some difficulties on the part of those who had had no opportunity of studying the catalogue, and who found that the order had been given without due consideration. The Grand Master of the Ordnance agreed with the War Minister only when he, in his turn, had perused one of the two supplementary catalogues that Ulysses had hurriedly prepared. They were equally convincing; only their binding was more modest. Morocco leather takes long to prepare, and Ulysses was in a hurry to sign.

The signing took place at the Sublime Porte with great pomp. The Grand Vizier and his immediate military and civil staffs were in uniform for the occasion. Ulysses, following Turkish etiquette, was dressed in an impeccable stambouline frock-coat from the best tailor in the Rue de Péra.

"For services rendered, for the loyalty and rapidity of the agreement," as the text of the parchment that was presented to him ran, Ulysses received from Abdul Hamid's own hands the Order of Iftikar, First Class, before the high dignitaries of the Ottoman Empire, all immense and so weighty with importance, corpulence, and honours that they strained their glittering uniforms to breaking point.

Tall, slender, and slightly stooping, beneath white hair, wearing his stambouline as an English lord wears evening dress, Ulysses looked as if he had never frequented anything but courts till he had wearied of them.

20

THE Turkish success had made Ulysses the cynosure of all big business magnates. All armament firms had worked for the order; the Americans, the English, the Germans, and the Austrians. Beaten in the last lap, they were slow to recover. In his hermitage in the Rue Malesherbes, Ulysses had to receive the proposals of all his defeated competitors. He accepted none and all of them.

He had decided to create an international armament system.

Up till then armament had been in the grip of patriotism. In every country the industry suffered from political limitations; it was shackled by the fear of supplying arms to a potential enemy. So, while all other great commerce had the whole world for its range, the armament field was limited by barriers that could not be crossed without the authority of the diplomats.

This conflict of incompetence was fraught with the unforeseen. The world's peace depends on men-of-war, and battles are generally lost by statesmen.

A company might let slip a brilliant transaction with a country that was believed hostile and which soon became an ally, while it had been authorized to arm some other country, believed friendly, whose arms were to be put to the test against the very men who had advised their furniture.

Ulysses, the quintessence of a little country whose exiguity guaranteed it against all short-sighted chauvinism, had a clearer outlook. He saw that all these restrictions served no purpose but that of encouraging the most surprising and inevitable mistakes; so he obviated the difficulty by placing it on a higher level. After long negotiations, he arranged that, through exchange of shares, secret collaborations, and a hundred other ways of a truly Byzantine subtlety, all the great armament firms would participate in all transactions. The sale of arms remained patriotic, and under the sway of diplomacy and War Offices; but the profits became international. The profit on the weapons of the herd should always remain beyond and above the herd. Having established the agreement, Ulysses remained the agent. From the depths of his retreat, he distributed orders, according to the political humour of each country where each armament firm had its factory. The most fault-finding War Office could have nothing to say against the deals that were carried out; the contemporary Prime Ministers were never thwarted in their Machiavellian schemes. So that under this regime the world armed itself more easily than ever before, and more patriotically. But to everybody's great joy, the profits of these armaments could not be tampered with by any meddlesome chauvinism.

For ten years Ulysses armed Europe from the Rue Malesherbes. He needed to chase after wealth no longer, for it came to him unbeckoned. Like his illustrious namesake, he could rest at last and indolently watch his sheep-shearing.

Perhaps the Odyssey is more of a symbol than a story. The wanderings of Ulysses the ancestor, his rebuffs and his triumphs, may represent the destiny of man running after fortune. Penelope with her webs is Fortune herself, who, faithful to the bold, awaits their home-coming and defends herself from mediocre and idle pretenders by weaving and unravelling her fugitive embroidery. Ulysses the descendant rested from his distant wandering, while the warp and woof of his destiny were weaving his fortune.

Profiting by the Young Turk movement, he placed a large order for cannons in Turkey, followed at a short interval by another in Bulgaria and a third in Serbia. At the moment he was occupied with Greece, which, in her turn, needed instruments of war.

At the fall of Abdul Hamid, the Turks, delivered from the bloodthirsty man of Yildiz, had exchanged the kiss of peace with their brothers in the Balkans. In the streets of Istanbul, Greek popes embraced Turkish muftis and Bulgarian popes, whose schism they pardoned and overlooked. The Bulgarians and Serbs, forgetting King Milan, Alexander of Battenberg, and the skirmish at Slivnitsa, embraced whenever they met; and, behind their kisses, Ulysses could gauge the fraternization of national consciences and foresee impending strife. He feared for his country. The Marquis de Lène had just introduced the Duke of Sparta, the Diadoch, and the future King Constantine, whom a military movement had just exiled to Paris.

Ulysses began by asking news of Venizelos, and the Duke of Sparta, although a Dane, replied: "May the devil take his father!" This un-Danish and essentially Greek expression made a good impression on Ulysses. He conceived, in that moment, for the Prince and all his family, an affection that never left him. He decided that the children of King George and Queen Olga, a Grand Duchess of Russia, had become real Greeks. Ulysses had always held himself mentally aloof from King George, owing to his icy patriotic scepticism. The sun of Attica had never been able to warm this Scandinavian soul. For her inexhaustible good works, he had pardoned Queen Olga her Slav origin, in thanks for the translation of the Gospel into modern Greek under her auspices. By his generous subscriptions to all Queen Olga's good works, since he had become rich, he had gained such support from her at the Russian Court that he was moved to indulgence. But this strictly local expletive, scented with the very thyme of Hymettus, moved him to look upon Constantine as the future Basileus of reconquered Byzantium.

Welding the wisdom of Nestor with the subtlety of the hero whose name he bore, he did his best to make the Duke of Sparta less uncompromising towards the Cretan who had just taken the destiny of their country into his hands. When, during their rare interviews, the Prince spoke of Venizelos and his revolt against the Prince's brother George, the former High Commissioner for Crete, Ulysses said laughingly:

"If his Greek is as rich in savour as your own, any Cretan would, of course, revolt," and Prince Constantine agreed, in spite of himself, that his brother George must certainly, with his sailor's vocabulary, have outraged the chaste ears of the Cretans, who are essentially lacking in Aristophanean humour.

Greece was going through difficult moments. The officers, proud of their glittering uniforms and ashamed of the sabres rusting in their scabbards, had determined to purge Greece of all her wordy statesmen, sick of their broken promises and daily verbiage in Parliament. But once the reins were in their hands, the soldiers did not know what to do with them. Like Diogenes, they were all in search of a man, and as Crete had been freed for twelve years, it was thither that their eyes were turned, and there that he was found. The officers had offered to join hands with Venizelos. He had accepted.

Greece, surprised and doubt-racked, with neither hope nor strength, gave herself to him as an abandoned woman, ruined and deceived by all her lovers,

[272]

gives herself to the first man whom she meets at the
street corner, provided that he be different from the
others. Lulled by phrases, put to sleep by the monotony of hollow periods, with sad awakenings at the
trumpet-blast of reality, she loved in this Cretan the
man who had weathered gunfire and been in disguise
now and then, the man who had rebelled against the
Turk; Hercules sweeping out the Augean stables was
how he appeared at first; then he declared himself a
die-hard conservative of the established order. The
disillusion was great. It almost sent him packing to
his island again. But soon, when the Greek Army under the Diadoch took Salonika in less than a month,
the wisdom of the man who had not wished to add
a dynastic crisis to all their other inevitable com-
plications began to be understood. It was seen that,
without that dynasty allied to the mightiest emperors,
the final acquisitions would have been much smaller.
The dream of reconquered Byzantium became an
almost tangible reality. And Byzantium without a
sovereign, without Constantine XII succeeding Constantine XI Palæologue, would have been absurd. The
instinct of the race became for the moment clearly
monarchist. In the popular imagination those two men
—Constantine and Venizelos—formed the synthesis of
the two highest glories of Greece. Following Basil II,
Constantine Boulgaroktonos—the Slayer of Bulgarians
—revived Byzantium, and Venizelos the Athens of
Pericles. Popular imagination turned these two men

into the duumvirate of Hellenic grandeur, the one representing classical wisdom, and the other Byzantine splendour. But in Athens, two men of equal power and popularity never agree for long. For Athens, the begetter of ideas and the destroyer of realizations, will always checkmate thought with thought and temperament with temperament, will always forestall that harmony which is the only womb of great deeds. As soon as anyone holds sway in Athens, he strives to hold it alone. The atmosphere of the Pnyx is atremble still with such a host of wonderful discussions that argument automatically comes to fling the opposite opinion to the ears of the multitude which has grown so avid of these tourneys that it can no longer do without them, though it knows all along that it will have to pay the piper. Thanks to the wisdom of Venizelos, Constantine came within a trice of grasping the sceptre of the Basileus, and, thanks to the sword of Constantine, Venizelos was already draped in the peplum of Pericles. But the ghosts of Æschines and Demosthenes decided otherwise. The echo of Pnyx could not but separate the warrior and the statesman, whose union alone could have been a constructive force, and whose rupture could only be as disastrous as the parties were great.

At the outbreak of the Great War, Ulysses saw all his dreams come true. To him, largest shareholder of all the great armament firms, every shot that was fired built up his fortune. But in the depths of his heart he could think only of his own little country. He saw her helpless at the cross-roads of all the highways of humanity, the fingers of her fragile hand projecting among the waves of the Eastern Mediterranean, that eternal melting-pot of destinies, where the Dorians had conquered Ionia, where St. Paul had preached the newfound God, where Antony had let slip the empire of the world, and where Don John of Austria had condemned the children of the Caliph to a lingering death. When he spoke with his old friend Kitchener, to whom Britain had just confided the organization of her armies, Ulysses understood for the first time the probable length of this war among wars. Revelling in the heart of contrary armaments, he was perhaps the only one to foresee the bitterness of the struggle and the immense destruction of men and empires, and, above all, principles. He knew that no human law, no treaty, no consideration or morality would temper or lighten the blows that would be taken and given. When Greece made her first declaration of neutrality, he boiled in his heart, and rejoiced in his brain; it was the neutrality of the lamb among the wolves. He wanted Greece to be, at least, a wolf-cub, he wanted to see her by the side of a probable winner, not torn to pieces by the whole pack. He would rather see her beaten even, under the wing of a great power, than alone and unarmed among the warriors.

He stated his views to the Greek Minister in Paris, summoned to his drawing-room for the purpose. He

[275]

replied to the arguments of the diplomat (who repeated the official theses formulated by the best scribe in Athens) by pointing to a worthy-looking little business man passing the window.

"Do you see that man? He is probably a shop-keeper down in the Avenue Marais. He doesn't do much business and owes no one a penny. I am one of the richest men in the world, but, like all great financiers, I may crash. Well, I can tell you that it would be better to go bankrupt in partnership with me than to be that man. The crumbs of my bankruptcy will make you far richer than he will ever be. Similarly it would be better for our country to be beaten along with Great Britain and France than to remain neutral, and mediocre."

As his arguments were not framed in chancellery jargon, the diplomat understood nothing of it.

The last word was the occupation of Greece by all the belligerents; Greece became a battlefield in which the Greeks took no part, the inactive spectators of their ravaged and blood-spattered household.

The Cretan, defeated by the incomprehension of some, the softness of others, and the dialectic of everybody, cherished an unconquerable faith in his heart. On the confines of the neutral country, he created a combatant Greece. Backed by a handful of men, he made Salonika his war-capital, Athens still remaining the capital of peace, sinking ever deeper in the slough of precarious security, humiliated and dishonoured by

[276]

daily insults. The handful of men became an army that Ulysses maintained at his own cost for more than a year. He took the budget of this new state into his own hands, and for one whole year he was the only man in history who has ever fed and housed a whole population. Thanks to him, the new Greece could stand firm by the side of her allies. She even had ministers to hinder the work of her warriors. It was no longer a question of mercenaries paid with foreign money, as Sarrail had wished. This general, who had begged for Greek volunteers to swell the stint of his own army, suddenly saw the figure of Venizelos rise beside him at Salonika. Macedonia, that wasted noman's-land of half a dozen armies, became Greece once more. Asking nothing of their allies but the weapons with which to fight, and paying for its own bread thanks to Ulysses, the Venizelist army re-established a national sovereignty that had long been compromised. Sarrail was against it from the start, and covered with insults the men who were shedding their blood for the work of which he was in command. Sarrail was recalled. Ulysses had had enough of him, and the wishes of a man who can hasten or delay the delivery of shells in war time are commands, although they are never pronounced in the open. Right up to the end, Ulysses took care to remain in the background. To put everyone off his guard, he had resigned all his directorships soon after war was declared. He did not want a Greek to take a seat among the English, the French, and the

[277]

Americans when there was a question of multiplying factories, delivering ammunition, and casting more cannons or less. Visible, he could but draw suspicion on his head; invisible, he was all-powerful.

There was constant talk of him in the Parliament lobbies. He haunted the imagination of all the oppositions. Sometimes, even governments were changed at his request, but the minister responsible for the change could always answer that he did not even know Ulysses by sight. He was the wraithy figure that lurked behind the gold and scarlet figures of the kings and field marshals and war ministers; he held nothing but the strings, but he held them all.

Having a drop of the blood of Icarus in his veins, Ulysses soon realized that the twentieth century was the era of bird-men. He paid for all the experience that the state budgets dared not risk. He rendered such services in this direction that France made him a Chevalier de la Légion d'Honneur, and England dubbed him Knight of the Bath. His investiture took place at Buckingham Palace and he received the accolade from King George V.

The chapel of the Order of the Bath was decked with his standard. At the chapters of the Order, he appeared in knee breeches and a feathered hat, a rapier at his side and the great cloak of the Order about his shoulders. Thenceforward in the United Kingdom, and at the court with the strictest medieval traditions in the world, he was Sir Odysseus Odyssides—

[278]

Sir Ulysses, son of Ulysses. It left him quite un-amazed. Two of his countrymen had already received the title from Queen Victoria, but only the Order of St. Michael and St. George. With the Order of the Bath he far outstrode them. He discovered his own language in his new title, and this put him at his ease immediately, for the word "Sir" comes from the French "Sire," which in turn springs from the Greek "Kyrios"—"Lord"—which, under Byzantium, was abridged to "Kyr" to precede the names of the Emperor and the Patriarch; and in Greece today it comes before the name of the most humble citizen of Greece. Ulysses answered his congratulators with the words:

"It is not much of an honour for a Greek. Sir Ulysses! Kyr Odysseus! In my own country, the mean-est sweeper is called Kyr Michali, and my own father was Kyr Odysseus before me!"

Ulysses had lived abroad for fifty years, and had become a great homogenite, the greatest of the "equally born"; and, like all his fellow-nobles, he could look upon the politics of King Constantine only with dis-favour. During the Great War, all the Greeks who were exiled in Egypt, America, France, and England were Venizelists. King Constantine's only partisans abroad were the few Greeks expatriated among the Central Powers. But whenever he met other Venizel-ists abroad, Ulysses remained strictly loyal to the mon-archist idea. From the first days of strife between the court and Venizelos, all, save a few snobs who were

[279]

used to mix with the royal family in Athens or at the watering places, became republicans. The Greek Republic was proclaimed by Greek colonies abroad long before it was proclaimed in Athens. But Sir Ulysses, Knight of St. Anne, of the Légion d'Honneur, and of the Bath, could only be a royalist. He owed his loyalty to the first and third of his ribbons. The republican Legion of Honour might have moderated this monarchist ardour, had it not been founded by Napoleon, an Emperor, and this origin put it on the side of King Constantine too, in spite of everything. A breast barred with red, green, or blue is not so free as a naked one, for an Order ribbon is always something of a rope that binds the movements of the body, and the heart that beats within. Among these glittering decorations, the modest ribbon of St. Saviour had little influence, but it tended also towards King Constantine. The Son of the Nazareth carpenter, adopted by Constantine the Great, has always been in favour at court. Thrones have always leant upon His altars, and His vicars have always supported crowns. All the honours of Ulysses seemed to tell him to keep King Constantine firmly seated on his throne, and Ulysses followed their prompting, so that, what with his profession, his pro-Entente interests, and his imperial ribbons, his brain was Venizelist and his heart Constantinian. The same terrible conflict was exercising all his compatriots.

21

✿✿✿

FOR several years Ulysses had been meditating a great rearrangement of his affairs. Having been the Dæmon of War, he now planned to evolve into an Angel of Peace. On the day that the Armistice was signed, Ulysses stood at his window and watched the crowds as they danced and howled. The oppression of four mortal years had broken loose; four years of discipline and constraint were being forgotten in one night of anarchy.

The grim life in trenches reeking of corpses that were ever removed and renewed, where death was in every breath of air, and whose only rhythm was marked by the bursting shells, had seemed so like a drawn-out suicide that the survivors, when it suddenly stopped, had a feeling of resurrection. For these sad remnants of humanity, all the four years of life in suspense condensed itself in one fantastic and undreamed-of night, so fraught was it with hope refound. The peace that followed that war of all humanity, in which the warriors had no longer been alone in the combat, where women, greybeards, and children had burrowed into the earth for refuge from the rain of iron that fell from the clouds, had something prophetic about it. The cannons' stillness seemed deeper after the tumult. Their voices were heard no longer, and the voices of men waxed to a hubbub. All the vital repressed energy, all the enforced chastity, all the suspended happiness, burst free in a great cry of joy and love. The husband returned to his wife, and the child found its mother again, knowing that, thenceforward, death would come no more to interrupt their kisses. Love of woman could go its old way. The family cottage was full once more, and looked out upon a skyline where the vine and the corn were ripening in the sun. Those eyes aghast with slaughter, those cheeks gaunt and drawn with weariness, those hands hardened by a toil with no other end than that of preparing or combating death, resumed their normal labours.

All Paris emptied into the streets. Everyone, quitting his lair, hastened to join the throng, to be in communion with all the rest, to swell the ranks of those who were already dancing underneath his windows, to take his place in the wild round that encircled the public squares, to mingle his voice with the rejoicing of his fellows.

For a considerable time Ulysses watched it all from his window. He felt its immense significance. For another generation, at least, engines of war could have but rare clients. Values would have to be transmuted. All he possessed had been guaranteed by war, once an eternal and realized menace. Thenceforward, works of peace alone could champion his fortune. The lofty pyramid of cannons and shells, on the summit of which his throne was perched, was crumbling at its very foundations. His castle of steel was nothing, now, but a card house, which the elbowing of that crowd howling its pacifist delirium at his gates might fling to earth with ease. He would have to change the groundwork of his fortune itself. His steel must flow into fresh moulds; and the moulds would have to be cast before all else. That night his dreams were full of railroads and ploughshares.

Before a fortnight was over he had assembled in his drawing-rooms all his representatives on the boards of the companies of which he was the biggest shareholder. Ulysses had chosen them less for their personal capacity—he relied entirely on himself for that—than for the qualities that were most highly prized in their own countries: in England, Ulysses had chosen resounding titles; in America, men of vast wealth; and, in France, the highest degrees, the most brilliant technicians.

All these English lords, American bankers, and French engineers met for the first time. Only now did they realize the titanic scope of the man who controlled them all. Beyond the immediate interests that each one represented, they had done no more than guess at the mighty ramifications of his power. Finding themselves face to face with each other in his presence, they all of a sudden realized the extent of his activities. Enterprises that had deemed themselves old rivals learned that they had worked hand in hand unwittingly, and bitter competitors found that, in their struggles, they had only completed one another. So many stages lay between his orders and their execution that most of Ulysses' agents were seeing their master for the first time. Others had never heard his name. Not one of them had ever dreamed of the number and length of the strings he held and manipulated as he chose.

As soon as they were all met and seated in a long row of armchairs, Ulysses, standing behind his vast writing-table, made them a little speech which the Marquis de Lène had prepared. The accent was his own and still smacked of Cephalonia.

"Gentlemen, I must thank you for the many services you have rendered me, and for your devotion to the interests that were entrusted to you. Your labours have been incessant for more than ten years; for the last four, they have been of an almost unbearable intensity. We can all have clear consciences; each one of us has done what he could in making the victory of Allied and friendly nations possible. But the war that has just finished will be the last one for the moment, for the long or short moment during which humanity must build itself up again by toil and peace. The cannon must make way for the ploughshare. I ask each one of you to give me, with the shortest possible delay, a plan for the transformation of the factories of which you are in charge into industries that serve peace. Speaking generally, the plan should be to make railways, agricultural implements, industrial machinery, and aeroplanes. The earth, which has been abandoned for four years, and the air, wherein the future of humanity lies, must be intensively exploited. But concentrate on the air—our aeroplanes must triumph as our cannons have triumphed. These are my thoughts, gentlemen. I await your plans. For the rehandling of your material and the transformation of your factories you shall have all the credit you need. Do not be afraid of big figures. Act well, act on a large scale, and, above all, act swiftly. But never forget to exercise the strictest economy. Spend all the money you need: not a penny more."

This short speech was followed by a long conference. Each one voiced his ideas on the point that interested him the nearest. Each director of a group of factories studied the possibilities of his group, in the country where it was situated. The secretaries took notes, and Ulysses filed all this information in his infallible memory. Like all men who seldom read and never write, his mind functioned better than the most carefully organized archives.

When his interlocutors strayed from the point or laboured in a tangle of details, he led them back to the track by an interruption or a remark that cut to the very heart of the question. The problem of labour interested him especially. Being of humble origin, and coming from a country with no other aristocracy than that of success, he felt none of the aloofness of his western collaborators from the people and their toil.

"A satisfied man is worth two unsatisfied ones," he would often repeat.

When the president of one of his large English trusts declared that the present government made the solution a very difficult one, Ulysses broke in: "Do not let that hinder you; the man who opposes us will go." When a project to be put into action in France was discussed, Ulysses asked the Marquis de Lène to see the Finance Minister that same night.

An American banker insisted at length on the difficulties caused by the Governor of a certain State. Ulysses drew him aside and explained in confidence that the Governor in question owed his election to Ulysses, and could not possibly oppose his wishes, and Sir Arthur Newfold wrote him a little note on this point immediately.

His collaborators had often seen difficulties that they had deemed insurmountable suddenly vanish; they had always felt behind the organization, of which they were members, the presence of a mysterious force which levelled their paths before their eyes. Now, they were face to face with that force and began to divine its power. When his scheme and the means by which

[286]

it might be realized had been understood by all his agents, Ulysses dismissed them, adding: "May God be with you."

These lords of industry and finance were astonished at such an unaccustomed expression. They had never heard it before in business language. The English and the Americans found in it the token of a deep-rooted belief, and the French were impressed by its exotic flavour.

For four years Ulysses followed the evolution of his work. He sacrificed a little of his fortune to consolidate the rest. He had to fight against routine and near-sighted prudence. He had to change entire boards of directors; and factory managers whom he had employed for ten years, but who had lost themselves in the rut of superannuated methods, had to cede their places to others. He had to encounter states and parliaments that were hard to handle. But, during the war especially, he had rendered too many public and private services to permit of opposition. So, at the chosen moment, a stubborn minister was dismissed, a loan failed or succeeded, the market rose or fell.

He manipulated the strings of world peace as he had manipulated the strings of world war. Too much capital and too many consciences were controlled by him that the sovereignty of his will should be opposed.

In his rare leisure moments, he worked for his country, for the catastrophe in Asia Minor had revived his patriotic sense. The exodus of a population of fifteen hundred thousand souls who had been hurled forth and cast up on the shores of a country impoverished by ten years of warfare, the slaughter and the misery of his brothers in blood and speech and religion, moved him profoundly.

Like all failure, this mismanagement irritated his warlike spirit. He felt great contempt, but greater pity, and gave without counting his giving. When the time came, he covered the Refugee Loan, which for this reason alone was covered twenty times in the London market.

A fortnight later his Greek secretary read out to him from an Athens paper a speech made by the Minister of Finance, in which it was said:

"The success of the loan proves that a wise policy bears fruit in season. This loan, twenty times covered, is an ample testimony of the confidence of the foreign markets. We have been judged by the great financiers, and our credit has triumphed——"

"Stop!" said Ulysses. "I can't go on listening to such rubbish. Those hornwearers carry presumption too far. If I had not had pity on the poor wretches, they would soon see the wisdom of their policy and their credit! If I choose to cover their loan, of course it will be covered twenty times over. Chicken-headed fools! Windbags! The only thing that they can control is the air they waste in clucking."

Under these churlish words, Ulysses concealed a

heart that yearned towards his country like a father's. He was an old man now, and his soul expanded in its power and goodness. For, finding no more obstacles in his path, all hate had died in him.

22

ULYSSES invited his three secretaries to dinner every Thursday, and at these weekly reunions he would give his thoughts free rein. His secretaries listened with attention, the better to understand his frame of mind and feel their way in the labyrinth of rapid instructions that he would give them during the week that followed; so their work was organized and enlightened by the communicative warmth of these banquets. The gatherings had been given this name by Sir Arthur, who, at Oxford, had been nourished on Greek letters and classical reminiscences, and was of an elegance worthy of Alcibiades. He would have preferred the Greek version "symposion," "drinking together," but the sobriety of Ulysses, who drank nothing but water, and troubled his head little enough with the wines that were served to his guests, dispelled any trace of a Dionysian atmosphere. The excellence of the fare, however, transformed Ulysses into a perfect Amphitryon. But as symposiarch, Sir Arthur found him mediocre. The Marquis de Lène, on the other hand, chiefly prized the banquets for their wealth of good food, and found nothing to criticize in his host's philoxeny. As for Dimitri Dimitropoulos, he had never been able to get used to the subtleties of French cooking. In the divine dialogues of Plato, he recognized and relished the everlasting back-taste of the resin-wine and the rancid oil. So, every Friday, after Ulysses' dinner, he sought consolation in a little Greek restaurant of the Latin quarter, where, if the meats and wines were Socratic, the dialogue had a more Bœotian smack.

During these banquets, the master would reveal himself to his secretaries. He had been in excellent humour lately, having just received a huge order for aeroplanes, and, if joy can be counted in millions, he was twice as happy as before. Towards the end of the meal, when the airiest of pineapple soufflés had just been served, Ulysses said to Sir Arthur:

"Tell me, Englishman, what you find most surprising in my career? . . ."

"May I be quite frank?" asked Sir Arthur.

"Completely," answered Ulysses.

"Well, sir, what surprises me most is that, without ever having played cricket, you should be a gentleman."

"Perfect!" cried Ulysses. "De Lène, Dimitri, do you hear? To be a gentleman, one must spend one's whole life running after balls, big or small, full or hollow. So it is astonishing that I, who have never thrown one in my life, should be a gentleman! The more one uses one's muscles, the less time remains to use one's intelligence. Sir Arthur is right; my country suffers too much from the exclusive cult of the brain. Besides, your love for balls has driven you to great things; as soon as you knew that the earth was round, you conquered it. When you realized that it was a ball, you grasped it and you are still holding it fast, as in rugby. I may even permit myself to say that you admire Sir Francis Drake less for beating the invincible Armada than for finishing a game of bowls before he set about it. But take care. The first ones to play that game—the one of the great ball, not the little ones you play at now —were not gentlemen. They were adventurers, like me. Through despising adventurers you have come to despise adventure, and decadence threatens any country that draws back from adventure. You are on the wrong track, with your dinner jackets, your good manners, and your formulas, which are as hollow as your balls. It is quite right to cling to the ball when the result of the game is at stake. But when the game is won, which it is in your case, one must not sit down on the ball. One is sure to fall off, one must aim towards another goal. It seems to me that you are resting on the ball that you have seized. Do not forget that it turns round, and that it is slippery. You will fall off, and, if you don't take care, someone else will catch hold of it."

Sir Arthur found Ulysses too direct. For the English, all precise and objective conversation is inadmissible. It seems tainted, even, with a certain vulgarity.

"Sir," interrupted Sir Arthur, with a touch of irony, "Socrates would have spoken in the same strain——"

"Do you mean, Sir Arthur," asked de Lène, "that, like Socrates, Sir Ulysses deserves the hemlock?"

"My dear friends," said Ulysses, "I know nothing of Socrates, or what he said. I had scarcely any schooling. But I know that he seldom went to the Stadium, and was a great reasoner. He was certainly no gentleman."

"Socratic sophism is first cousin to untruth and its principal ally," said Sir Arthur, "and we English hate untruth——"

"Now I have got you, Sir Arthur," said Ulysses. "We Greeks sometimes tell lies, but, on the other hand, we often tell the truth. You English never lie; but, contrariwise, you never tell the truth. All personal and clear questioning is banned in England; you have made to yourselves a puritan language, stiff and muffled in long folds of formulas that never reveal the anatomy of the thought that they may clothe. Between the ostracism of the indiscreet, and the false modesty of your language, the truth never transpires. It only shows a corner of its face, a painted corner. More, you have proscribed all personal ideas; every single one of your rare ideas is a national one, and your interests become your principles. Should your inter-

[293]

ests change, it suffices you to reinterpret the principle behind which it hides. You have a chosen few who are responsible for this adjustment, and through these historic contradictions, everyone remains honest and truthful. You never lie, because your truth changes with necessity. In other words, you never say what you think, because you never think at all. But you always believe what your leaders think is most useful for you to say."

"All the same, we have had great philosophers, great poets, and great scientists," Sir Arthur objected.

"Doubtless," continued Ulysses, "but you have never believed that they were gentlemen. You profit by them as one profits by labour, which does useful work, but with which one is careful to avoid all intimacy; and, taking it all in all, your system is not a bad one. Yours is a nation that plays, while a chosen few are thinking; we Greeks are a nation that thinks while a chosen few play. And as intellectuals do not play at ball, the Greeks play at politics, and it is very much more dangerous."

Sir Arthur held his peace. He hated reason for reasoning's sake.

De Lène, on the contrary, was addicted to the vice of syllogism as profoundly as any Greek. He caught the ball on the bounce, and began with a pun in French.

"Sir Ulysses," he said, "what I admire so much in you is the wonderful way in which you have applied

[294]

la règle de Troie. The Rule of Three, the Rule of Troy."

"I don't understand," said Ulysses.

"I will put it more clearly," de Lène went on. "Your Homeric namesake entered Troy in a wooden horse. You fled from Khartoum in a wooden coffin. That is what I mean by the Rule of Troy. Triumph achieved through inspired and transcendental ruse—Zeus becoming a swan to lie with Leda, the comrades of Ulysses escaping the Cyclopes under the bellies of their rams, and a thousand other subterfuges with which your mythology and history teem. If you had been English or French, the Mahdi would have had your head. But you had his. And your country is just the same as yourself, it has ruined all its masters. Just as your gods turned themselves into swans, your countrymen contrived to make themselves small to avoid the buffets of fortune; and then, at the propitious moment, when it profited them to be dwarfs no longer, they found a poet who turned them into giants.

"A party of Medes and Persians, having followed up a daring raid as far as the gates of Athens, was driven back. Your poets turned this incident into the rout of a mighty host. They sang a Leonidas fighting with a handful of men against so great a multitude that its arrows eclipsed the sun; and a Cynægirus who held fast an enormous trireme by his teeth alone. They sang so well that the fatalistic and indolent Asiatics, instead of returning in force, sank into lethargy, dream-

[295]

ing that they had been defeated by a race of Titans. And this hallucination, engendered by the harmony of your periods, sowed such germs of disintegration that a few years later they fled in millions before Alexander and his scanty Macedonian phalanges.

"Even the Romans never plumed themselves with your entire conquest. Dazzled by your subtle reasonings and by the music of your poems, they wavered and softened at your touch. Your god Ares, whom, as Mars the War God, they had adopted long before, led them from victory to victory, but when he beguiled them back into his own country, he effaced himself before the altars of the Muses and Graces, and the stern Romans were vanquished in their turn. In Athens, even those austere warriors felt that they must labour in your service, and when their roads and their aqueducts had been built under the mocking eyes of a population that was idle through elegance, and whose nostrils were outraged by the rank sweat of these hard-working and cloddish soldiers, the Romans retired behind the Adrian gate, to barricade themselves, almost, against that superior disdain.

"Your arm is often weak. But your thought, your writing, and your language are invincible. It is the Rule of Three, and it is the Rule of Troy. It is the same Greek miracle that Renan felt, as he could not but feel it, when he wrote of the most surprising example of your success. For the Greeks alone have known how to worst the Jews.

"The Jews are an austere folk, hermetically self-contained, who for thousands of years have believed themselves the chosen of God, and the only interpreters of His law; a breed of warrior-saints and prophets, preparing the ways of the Lord and awaiting the Messiah. He was long in coming. But, as soon as a few Jews became Hellenized, He appeared. All He did was to affirm the ancient law of Moses, fulfilling it a little, scarcely modifying it at all; and what He said in Aramaic is no longer important. But what He has been made to say in Greek has turned the whole world upside down. First the Hellenizing St. Paul; later the Fathers of the Greek Church, adopted Him and transmuted Him into a Greek philosopher, an Eleusinian *myste*, building of Him, on Him, and all around Him a new Olympus, with a Holy Trinity, a court of saints and demigods, and a worldly *agora*, where, for two thousand years (since St. Clement of Alexandria and Origen, to Loyson and Tyrrell, passing through St. Gregory of Nazianza, St. Basil, and St. Thomas Aquinas), Socrates, Plato, and Aristotle live again. You have performed the impossible; you have taken Jewish thought by storm, and remoulded it to your fancy, till the god whom it engendered and misunderstood has become a Greek, and lives for ever."

"All that you say pleases me mightily," interrupted Ulysses, "although you are too erudite for me to be able to check your theories. What do you think about it, Sir Arthur?"

[297]

"I was thinking about the Dempsey-Carpentier match," replied Sir Arthur, laughing.

"And you, Dimitri . . . ?"

Dimitri gathered himself together. Being a laureate of Athens University and the Sorbonne, he felt that it would ill become him to talk lightly on such a vast subject. After a long silence, pregnant with compact learning, he said:

"The French think in paradoxes. To answer seriously, I would have to read forty volumes from end to end, and write at least five——"

"I yield before that menace," answered Ulysses, "and beg you not to explain. If you ever write those five books, I promise that I'll pay for their publication, and not read a word of them; a Greek never reads what another Greek writes, unless it is a note of hand, or an order. But let us change the subject. De Lène, you have told us all about the past history of Greece. What do you think of us nowadays?"

"Nowadays?" said de Lène. "Why, I admire you more than ever. . . . You are practically French. . . ."

"The Rule of Troy," interrupted Ulysses, "gives way before the Rule of Three—the rule of the French, the rule of thrift, and the rule of accurate book-keeping! While you were singing our praises, I was certain that your peroration would be 'Vive la France!' No Frenchman can finish a speech without shouting or thinking it."

At these words Sir Arthur burst out laughing. The
noisy and imperative chauvinism of the French is the
reason why the Englishman—a silent patriot—and the
Frenchman—an articulate one—will never understand
each other.

"Do you know where your strength lies?" continued
Ulysses. "In your purses, with their watertight com-
partments: one for notes, one for silver, and a third for
coppers. The extraction of a piece of money is such a
long and complicated process that it gives you time to
think twice; for the coin emerges with difficulty. It is
so well lodged, so fondled, that it hesitates to venture
into the light of day. It is so warm in its nest that it
lays and hatches little ones. Your wallets are treasure-
caskets, wherein your holy relics are guarded, each one
catalogued according to its importance and its virtue.
Our pockets, with their disorder, and their continual
goings and comings, are more like brothels that one
quits in a hurry. Everything is provisional there. They
are just the stopping places of a moment, caravanserais,
while your wallets are real homes that are never emptied, aswarm with more and ever more children, whose
birth is inevitable in such a sure and comfortable nest.
And they are just like your brains, where your ideas
are all arranged in pigeon-holes; no confusion or disorder. When you take them out, your thoughts emerge
as if they were on parade, perfectly equipped and dis-
ciplined, with the hierarchy and function of each unit

[299]

clearly defined. For you, discussion is a pitched battle, no wild unreasoned charge that might breed disorder and defeat."

"I thought, on the contrary," de Lène objected, "(and it is the general opinion too), that ours was the country of French 'volatility' and disorder. Surely, Germany is more like the picture that you have just painted of us. . . ."

"I would not be where I am," resumed Ulysses, "had I shared the general opinion. You have just defeated Germany, and in the memoirs of the principal actors in her defeat, Germany is beginning to confess, and these confessions prove that I am right. Order, in Germany, is a thin horizontal plasm; in France it lies deep down beneath the surface. In Germany, the land is orderly, in France the individual. There, organization is clear, and heads are muddled; here, it is just the other way about: organization is muddled but heads are clear. In France, all that meets the eye has a disordered appearance; but the things that cannot be seen —the soul, the mind, and the heart—are admirably adjusted. In Germany, it is exactly the contrary. The German Army was better organized than the French, but Foch was more organic than Ludendorff, and that was why he won. If Foch had been in command of the German Army, Paris would have been taken and the battle of the Marne would never have occurred. In every war, the time comes when the man behind the gun, as the English say, counts more than the gun

[300]

itself, and that is what gave you victory. Order on the surface is apparent; interior and profound order is not, and so the Germans were thought to be serious and the French superficial. A flock of sheep is better organized than a troop of horses, but each single sheep is inferior to each single horse, and when there is a prairie-fire (I have seen it myself, in America), the sheep lose their heads, while the horses trample the flames and extinguish them beneath their concerted hoofs. In normal times, your deeply and thoroughly organized individualities split up into factions, and govern you badly; but in the Evil Hour they weld themselves into one provisional, but superior, whole, and come through unscathed."

"At Valmy," interrupted de Lène.

"You know nothing of your history," continued Ulysses. "I know men. My dear de Lène, I come from an island where madness reigns, and madness interests me. I have built three asylums. I have studied the question. And lo! France is the country with the lowest percentage of madmen in the world, and I attribute it entirely to the wallets in which you keep your money, and your thoughts."

"Sir Ulysses," said de Lène, "you have overthrown Sir Arthur and myself. Are you going to spare Dimitri, your countryman, and our colleague? Can this banquet finish without him, too, hearing a few truths from above?"

"Dimitri is a good boy," said Ulysses; "he is well

brought up and sober. But he will never be any good. He will spend his life admiring his diplomas; and for fear of being untrue to them, he will never use them at all, otherwise than theoretically. Their only use will be to marry him off to a wife with a good dowry. Do you think he went to Athens University and the Sorbonne to learn? Not at all. His only ambition was to acquire a parchment stating that he was a man of learning. Since he has got it, he has never opened another book, but he unfolds his diploma like a banner, a coat-of-arms, a patent of nobility. It will procure him a rich, and probably ugly, young woman, and that marriage is the limit and crown of all his ambitions. She will nourish and support his household, and he will be the doctor of law who knows everything and does nothing. In the café, he will close all arguments with the words: 'I, who am a doctor of law at the University of Paris, tell you . . .' For the Greek respects an academic degree as long as it remains academic; Dimitri will be listened to in silence as long as he is content with stringing sonorous phrases together, with no practical result. But if, through self-admiration, he decides to impose himself at last, he will perhaps embark on a political career. Then, if he makes that blunder, his degrees will lose all their glory, having abandoned their academic virginity to become instruments of possession and concrete power. Then they will be considered as bits of soiled paper covering the greatest stupidity and the most abysmal ignorance.

Dimitri will be treated as a mountebank and an impostor.

"Greece is divided into graduates and non-graduates; the first exploit their parchments, the others exploit the earth and the sea; and especially the air, the breath of the would-be purchaser and the would-be vender; the first live in mediocre security, the others struggle and triumph and work, raise themselves, fall down again, and make and unmake Greece. You see Dimitri every day. Sir Arthur plays tennis, golf, and polo; and you, de Lène, read every book that comes out; Dimitri neither plays nor reads; he meditates on his parchments. And Greece is full of young men just like him. I have not set foot there for fifty years, and they will have me there only when I am dead; for I like the earth of Greece. I want to rest there, but only when I am beyond waking at the eloquence of university graduates. Greece is torn between those who think and those who express themselves. Few Greeks can do both. The Greek language is a difficult one, and they who thoroughly possess it astonish, and impose themselves upon, their fellows. So Greece is governed by lawyers and grammarians. The only thing that saves her is that no one dreams of keeping the laws voted by the lawyers in the grammarians' language."

"Perhaps that is what Plato foresaw, when he wanted to banish the poets from his republic," suggested de Lène, "and the Roman who said: 'Beware of the man with only one book.'"

[303]

"What I say is: beware of the Greek with no book at all," said Ulysses, "for the Greek with even one book is so proud of it that he can never cast loose from it again. Instead of becoming the book's master, he becomes its slave. When a Greek has learning he understands nothing; and when he knows nothing he understands everything."

"But if your education had been more complete," said Dimitri timidly, "perhaps, with your genius, you would have done still more. . . ."

"What more could I have done?" asked Ulysses. "I have made my fortune several times, in three continents and five or six different countries. If I did not actually make the World War, it was I, more than anyone else, who provisioned it. . . . If I had had your education, I would have ended up as town clerk in Argostoli. . . . Don't forget, Dimitri, that that was what you were when I took you into my service."

With these words, Ulysses rose.

The banquet was finished.

23

✿✖✿

WITH the passage of time, Ulysses died in his London flat.

His will, drawn up in Greek, began with the words:

"In the name of the Holy Trinity, of unique essence, I, Ulysses, son of Ulysses . . ."

For a homogenite, the will was a work of art. He knew that it would be published in all the newspapers and discussed in all the coffee-houses, that his life would be judged according to it. A reflection of his soul would be read therein, and his memory would be insulted or applauded in connexion with his last wishes. Everyone would discuss his legacies and his omissions, and the genealogists would find him seventh cousins, and men who had protected him in his youth, whom he might have forgotten.

"Do you hear? He forgot that poor Marigo, the daughter of his mother's cousin, who hasn't even enough to eat."

"Do you hear? He hasn't left a drachma to the

grandson of Barba Yanni, who used to give him bread when he was running about the streets of Athens barefoot. You know that Gerasymos, the barber who married the daughter of Dimo, at Livathia, is his godson? The whole village remembers, and think of it, only Ulysses forgot! . . ."

In all the coffee-houses throughout Greece, but especially in his native island, commentary runs its course. In the little cafés, the comments are usually of an intimate kind, while in the big Athenian cafés, especially in the Café Zacharatos in the Syntagma, the comments are more general.

"Do you hear? He has left only thirty million drachmas to charity. What difference would it have made to him to have left twice, three times, ten times as much? He doesn't need it now. It shows a great vulgarity. How shall I put it? He never knew how to become a gentleman. Besides, what more can one expect of a Cephalonian?"

The island is cited because it is the birthplace of Ulysses. Had he come from Chios or Volo, or any other part of Greece, the opprobrium would have fallen on his cradle just the same. There is not a town throughout Greece that escapes insult. Each one is vilified by the Greeks from elsewhere, and each one stands by its own children.

But the will of Ulysses was a masterpiece. It forgot nothing and nobody. His immense fortune, one of the biggest in the world, was divided into many parts, each one carefully pondered over. He had remembered his country; then his village; the Sudan, where he had first proved his mettle; Egypt, where he had enjoyed a brief day of triumph; the two Americas; France, which had become his second motherland; and England, which had honoured him more than any other country. In each land he endowed chairs, contributed to hospitals, and relieved distress. He left graduated sums, assuring an easy life for ever, to all his relations, even to the eighth degree. In Athens, he founded an important technical and professional school, with the commentary: "There is a plethora of lawyers and doctors in Greece; there are not enough workmen and agriculturists. I want my countrymen to learn to work more with their hands and less with their tongues." Although he had foreseen all that could be foreseen and remembered all that could be remembered, Ulysses did not escape criticism, for in Greece criticism comes easily and praise is scanty.

As he left to everyone and everything sums that were so much greater than any that the narrowly limited Athenian financial imagination was able to conceive, his legacies went uncarped at, and all the criticism fell upon the last paragraph of his will. It ran thus:

"For the honour of my country and of my race, I refuse none of the honours that any may wish to pay to my mortal remains. But I want to be buried at Livathia, the village of my birth, beside my blessed mother, and in the garb of a beggar, like that which I wore during the first years of my life."

Franciscan humility is foreign to the Greek mind, so the return of Ulysses to his native land as he had left it was taxed with clownery.

"Do you hear? After eating up the world's money, and being covered with honours, he treats us to humility and poverty. Whom is he laughing at, do you think?"

As soon as one displays a shade of lyricism in Greece, one is accused of mockery.

Ulysses' funeral in London was without precedent. It was a mixture of the pomp and etiquette reserved to a Commander of the Order of the Bath and the Byzantine pomp and mysticism of the Orthodox Church.

The Greek church in Bayswater was aglitter with uniforms. The mourners were led by the Greek Minister in London and the personal representative of King George V. The crowd was made up of a delegation of the Order of the Bath, all the great figures in politics and finance, and a great number of the British aristocracy. The service was conducted by the Metropolitan of Thyateres, Archbishop of all Western Europe, assisted by the chaplain of the Order of the Bath and all the archimandrites of the Orthodox churches of France and England.

The Greek priests, with their long hair and beards, clad in their golden copes, looked like glittering Byzantine icons. Beside the heavy coffin of wrought

[308]

bronze, three pages of the British Court bore the dead man's decorations on velvet cushions. The Archbishop of Canterbury, in cassock and surplice, stood to the right of the archiepiscopal throne.

With the progress of the requiem, the nave was filled with incense; grey-blue wisps of smoke lingered fleetingly about the candle flames; the choir of male voices, deep and grave, seemed to fall from the sky itself; and when the Metropolitan pronounced the verses where St. John Chrysostome comments upon the book of Ecclesiastes—"Oh, vanity of vanities, all is vanity, what is the use of gold?"—even the English seemed to feel that this strong and harmonious Greek, with its slow and unseizable rhythm, was the one language chosen by God to reveal Himself to man.

The absolution was given by the chaplain of the Order of the Bath, then by the Archbishop of Canterbury, Primate of England, and lastly by the Greek Metropolitan.

Whatever Ulysses' sins might have been, his soul could not but be lightened by so many absolutions.

The Greek Government sent a battle-cruiser to Portsmouth, to bear Ulysses' body to Greece, and a special train was put at the disposal of the Greek Minister.

For this latterday Ulysses, his Odyssey continued even after his death, for in Athens his obsequies began again with a new vigour.

His funeral was not a national, it was a Panhellenic

one. From the largest Greek colonies abroad, from Khartoum, Cairo, Alexandria, New York, Paris, and London, representatives had come to honour their posthumous benefactor.

The clergy alone occupied half the Metropolitan Cathedral. Beside the presiding Metropolitan of Athens were ranged all the metropolitans of the Holy Synod of the Autocephalous Greek Church, the delegates of the Œcumenical Patriarch of Constantinople, and of the Patriarchs of Alexandria and Jerusalem. Ulysses was even honoured by the presence of two Œcumenical Patriarchs who had abdicated, who gnawed at their tethers and chafed at their idle tiaras in Athens. Only the royal family was lacking, with its noble stature, its Grand Master of Ceremonies, and its aides-de-camp, for Greece was already a republic, and, save for the brilliant vestments of the clergy, the honours she paid him were tarnished with black frock-coats, badly worn and of mediocre cut. The ministers, the Government, the Mayor of Athens, the Municipal Council, the Army, and the Navy filled the rest of the nave and even overflowed onto the pavement, leaving a number of notables to be shouldered, paralysed, and lost in the mob that invaded the square, the neighbouring streets, and even the church itself. The painstaking officials had arranged the precedence and assigned the places in vain, as the popularity of the dead man—whom nobody had seen during his life—upset all their careful arrangements, and pushed a common cigarette-pedlar next to the President of the Republic, and a young sub-lieutenant into the midst of the ministers. The Finance Minister, who was particularly interested in Ulysses' will and the bequests by which the treasury would profit, never succeeded in disentangling himself from the crowd, and stood in the open air for three long hours, meditating on the Kingdom of Heaven, where the first will be last.

When all the prayers and chanting were finished, Ulysses was pardoned by the absolution of all Orthodoxy. All the metropolitans—there were twelve of them—repeated the words of forgiveness in turn; and even the two former Patriarchs wanted to cap it with their authority (which, though it was still supreme in heaven, was lost on earth for ever). After these twelve archiepiscopal absolutions, following those lavished in London and confirmed by two Patriarchs, the devil had certainly lost the few claims on his person that Ulysses, during a long and stormy life, might have given him.

When the Metropolitan of Athens pronounced the epilogue of the Orthodox funeral office: "Receive the last kiss," only the President of the Republic was able to touch the enormous catafalque with his lips. The Prime Minister attempted to follow his example, but the movement of the crowd, turning simultaneously about, to quit the asphyxiating church, areek with incense, breath, and perspiration, almost upset him onto the bier, which was rocking under the pressure of the people.

But Greek crowds have a strong feeling of gregarious respectability. The evacuation of the church took place without any violent disorder or disarray. Everyone drew back a little to let the coffin go by. It was preceded by the metropolitans, and followed by all those whose especial duty it was to follow it. The other lower dignitaries never saw the coffin, or their top hats, again.

It had been decided that the funeral orations should be delivered at the church entrance. There were twelve of them; one for each apostle, it would seem. There were long and short ones. There were inaudible ones and incomprehensible ones. Some were in classical Greek, others in demotic, and they endowed the defunct with all the virtues. He was a hero and a saint. A model of all perfection and renunciation, he had been a martyr to honest toil, and to devotion to the common weal. He was praised, dithyrambed, and canonized. He deserved a place on the altar. Indeed, there was a young poet who climbed up on a lamp post and declaimed a poem of fifty lyrical, tragical, and emphatic verses in the voice of a herald and with the gestures of a windmill. The Premier, who was a powerful orator, said only a few words; but he said them in such a voice and with such a rhythm that a flood of enthusiasm ran through the crowd. For the Athenian agora is still susceptible to resounding phrases. A shout, springing from a heart that had been stirred to its innermost depths, pierced the air, mastering the crowd-wide rumour:

"Long live the deceased!"

This re-echoing antiphony provoked no hilarity, so great is the truth that the value of words depends on the humour of crowds alone. An immense murmur, coming from a hundred thousand throats in the grip of the moment's solemnity, drowned the voice of the orator:

"Long live the deceased!"

And this contradictory murmur accompanied the remains of Ulysses all through the streets, which were lined with soldiers presenting arms, and children from every school and orphanage, to the Piræus, where it was hoisted aboard a destroyer that sailed away with it to Cephalonia.

The whole island was waiting for the prodigal son who was coming home covered with honour and glory and gold. His own family alone made up a crowd. The whole of his village joined in the funeral procession, along with a few neighbouring thorps, and everyone seemed to be a close relation of the dead man.

The congregation of cousins gathering about the bier grew in size like a rolling snowball.

But, in accordance with his will, the last office was simple. Only the pope of his own village officiated, and this pope was the own son of the one who had baptized him. For the priesthood, in Greece, is often hereditary; a cure of souls is an heirloom that one tries to keep in the family. Faithful to his testament, a few expert old women, in funeral weeds, stripped his embalmed corpse of the evening dress in which it had been clad in London. The eyes of the old peasant women had never seen such a coat, nor so many gilded and enamelled stars. They cried a miracle. Later on, they used to say that the stars of heaven had fallen from the sky to settle on the breast of their illustrious and holy fellow-villager. When he had been stripped, they arrayed him in a pair of torn and patched trousers, and a ragged coat whose fabric scarcely held together; and shod him with tattered and soleless shoes, while the pope was droning:

"Vanity of vanities, all is vanity . . ."

His native land received Ulysses back in the same garb as that in which he had left it seventy-one years before. The sisters of Ulysses, who had all outlived him (for women die hard in Greece), wept for four hours, all the way uphill from the port to the village. When they saw him lowered into the gaping hole beside his mother's tomb, their wails became shrieks. For three days, while they received their visits of condolence, which were intensified by the newly acquired wealth of the mourners, they broke the funeral silence at almost regular intervals with loud wailings and groanings, for nowhere do women wail louder and longer than in Greece.

In this wise Ulysses, the son of Ulysses, lived, died, and was buried. May the earth, over which he wandered so far, rest lightly upon him!

May his memory be green for ever in the heart of that famous race, whose history throughout the centuries has been, a little, his own. May he, too, find a poet to sing his misfortunes and his triumphs, and his wanderings in the eternal wooden horse of Troy, which forces the gates of the strongest battlements. For, even better than his ancestor:

"Of many men he knew the towns and read the minds," and profited by them all.